The Book of Style for Medical Transcription, 3rd Ed.

Workbook

The Association for Healthcare Documentation Integrity

Lea M. Sims, CMT, AHDI-F

Publisher: Association for Healthcare Documentation Integrity
Author/Managing Editor: Lea M. Sims, CMT, AHDI-F
Copyeditor: Kristin Wall
Professional Programs Manager: Kelly Kappmeier
Interior Design: Lea M. Sims, CMT, AHDI-F
Cover Design: Network Media Partners, Inc.
CD-ROM Development & Design: Bob Bryan & Laura Bryan, CMT, AHDI-F (Bob's PCWerks)
Printer: CADMUS, Port City Press – A Cenveo Company

AHDI
4230 Kiernan Avenue, Suite 130
Modesto, CA 95356
800-982-2182
www.ahdionline.org

CADMUS, Port City Press
1323 Greenwood Rd.
Baltimore, MD 21208

DISCLAIMER

Care has been taken to confirm the accuracy of the information present and to describe generally accepted practices and represent common practical scenarios. However, the authors, editors, and publisher are not responsible for errors or omissions or for any consequences from application of the information in this book and make no warranty, expressed or implied, with respect to the currency, completeness, or accuracy of the contents of the publication. Application of this information in a particular situation remains the professional responsibility of the practitioner.

ISBN 978-0-935229-61-5

Printed in the United States of America

To purchase additional copies of this book, call our member services department at (800) 982-2182 or purchase this text online at www.ahdionline.org.

Look for AHDI on Facebook, Twitter, and Linked In under *Association for Healthcare Documentation Integrity.* Visit our blog at www.ahdilounge.blogspot.com.

Dedication

For every MT with an eye for detail
Who believes that a standard should always prevail,
Who takes extra minutes to make it "just so"
And knows where all pesky commas should go,
Who seeks to know always just what to do,
This Book of Style Workbook is written for *you*!

And if you're an MT who just hasn't a clue,
Well...this workbook is written just for *you, too*.

Lea M. Sims, CMT, AHDI-F

Acknowledgements

Having spent the last three years or so with my head down in manuscript preparation of one kind or another, I have truly come to appreciate the team effort it takes to bring a book to press, especially technical manuals and books such as *The Book of Style for Medical Transcription* and this new companion workbook. Without the support and assistance of so many, we would not have this ancillary material for medical transcription students, educators, and practitioners.

As acknowledged in the first edition of this workbook, I am grateful for the visionary thinking of Claudia Tessier, RHIA, CAE, and Sally C. Pitman, who along with their colleagues first conceived of a resource for medical transcription standards for style. That early collaboration became the "gold" standard that paved the way for future editions of the current Book of Style, including the 3rd edition text that is in circulation today and to which this workbook offers a supportive framework of practical application.

Special thanks goes out to the following individuals whose expertise and support were critical to the development of this text and to its timely release:

- *Kristin Wall, AHDI-F,* for outstanding copyediting, proofreading, and making sure this text meets AHDI's rigorous standards for professional excellence.

- *Laura Bryan, CMT, AHDI-F,* for her technical expertise and innovative thinking and for being one of our industry's most valuable assets.

- *Kelly Kappmeier* for dynamic project management of this publication and keeping all of us on track getting this book to market on time.

- *Jay Vance* for lending a "voice" to the dictation of the majority of our audio files, housed originally in the first edition of this text and carried over now to this one.

Finally, I want to thank my family for love, support, and patience when zealous focus on a manuscript "overtakes" me for a season. Grady, Peyton, Madison, and Aiden—you make every second worthwhile.

Lea M. Sims, CMT, AHDI-F

Table of Contents

How to Use This Book

This workbook is designed to be used as a supplemental study guide in coordination with *The Book of Style for Medical Transcription*, 3rd edition—either in print format or online subscription, alone or through Benchmark KB. Students and practitioners should coordinate the practical application exercises in this chapter with those corresponding chapters in the Book of Style.

Each chapter contains chapter objectives to help educators, particularly, align the objectives in the corresponding Book of Style with course objectives for transcription style as established by their educational programs as well as those in the AHDI Model Curriculum. In addition to objectives, virtually all chapters in this text offer the following practical applications:

- Tips and strategies for creating flashcards and ancillary study materials to augment the approach to this information.
- Multiple-choice questions provided in each chapter are designed to assist the student and/or practitioner with applying standards outlined in this text to questions of a type and format similar to those that would be encountered on AHDI credentialing examinations. Answers to these questions can be found at the end of each chapter.
- Proofreading exercises that allow the reader to apply the principles of style outlined in the chapter to simulated editing scenarios where identification of error is critical to quality assurance in a transcription setting. Answers to these exercises can be found at the end of each chapter.
- Corresponding dictation practice via dictated .mp3 files housed on the CD-ROM that accompanies this text. Early chapters that focus on the legal record, formatting, privacy, and security do not have accompanying dictation exercises. Answers to the dictation practice exercises can be found in Appendix A in the back of the book as well as on the CD-ROM itself.

You'll note that chapters 25-28 of the Book of Style are not addressed in this text. These industry trends and standards chapters represent information greatly subject to change given the rapid evolution of technology and the constantly changing standards for documentation and data exchange that exist in the industry. MTs should maintain professional membership in AHDI to stay abreast of these trends, drivers, and changes on the horizon for our sector.

CHAPTER 1

Types, Formats, and TATs

Learning objectives for this chapter:

- ✓ Understand and apply *Book of Style* (BOS) standards related to document types, formats, and turn-around times.
- ✓ Accurately identify these standards via multiple-choice questions that prepare you for AHDI credentialing examinations.
- ✓ Apply your knowledge of these standards to proofreading/editing exercises that prepare you for practical application in the workplace and on AHDI credentialing examinations.

Introduction

Chapter 1 of this text provided an in-depth overview of industry standards and expectations related to the legal medical record. Understanding the *process* for documentation of patient care encounters is a critical first step in being able to apply informed judgment in the transcription process. With changes occurring every day in the way health information is captured and repurposed, it is important for anyone entering the field of healthcare documentation to be familiar with document types, formatting standards, and turn-around time expectations for all settings and specialties, regardless of the work setting in which you may ultimately find yourself. Keep in mind that healthcare documentation standards are constantly changing, and standardization of document formats will continue to shape how health information is captured and how the standards outlined this chapter will continue to be applied.

Tips and Strategies for this Chapter:

- *Read the chapter thoroughly, highlighting or underlining references that are unfamiliar to you, including acronyms and organizational names mentioned in this section.*
- *Make flashcards or note cards of the document types, including report subheadings that are part of the ASTM standards for formats. Keep these nearby as you transcribe to learn and apply these common formats.*
- *Familiarize yourself with the chapter index found in the margin on the first page of this chapter in your BOS (page 3) and practice navigating the chapter using the index.*

Exam Prep Assessment

Apply your understanding and knowledge of Chapter 1 to the multiple-choice exam prep questions below.

1. All of the following are true of major headings in a medical report except:

   A. express major section headings using all capitals.
   B. always insert obvious headings that are not dictated.
   C. double space between major headings of reports.
   D. use initial caps only for subheadings.

2. Which of the following major headings is not part of a SOAP note?

   A. SUBJECTIVE
   B. OPERATION
   C. ASSESSMENT
   D. PLAN

3. Any specimen that is sent for pathologic evaluation will undergo which kind of evaluation?

   A. Gross
   B. Microscopic

C. All of the above
D. None of the above

4. Which of the following major headings is typically found in an autopsy report?

   A. CHIEF COMPLAINT
   B. DIAGNOSTIC STUDIES
   C. GROSS FINDINGS
   D. HOSPITAL COURSE

5. Which of the following refers to a document type dictated by a physician on subsequent visits after a patient's initial evaluation in the office?

   A. SOAP note
   B. Follow-up note
   C. Progress note
   D. All of the above

6. According to the Joint Commission, an admitting history and physical examination must be completed within no more than ____________ hours of inpatient admission.

   A. 6
   B. 12
   C. 24
   D. 48

7. Which of the following is transcribed correctly?

   A. LUNGS: clear.
   B. LUNGS: Clear.
   C. LUNGS: clear.
   D. LUNGS: Clear.

8. A single character space should be used:

   A. after an opening quotation mark.
   B. before a hyphen.

C. at the end of a sentence after the punctuation mark.
D. All of the above.

9. Which format for correspondence requires all text to begin flush with the left margin?

A. Full block
B. Modified block
C. Indented
D. Memorandum

10. What is the standard turn-around time for consultation reports?

A. 4-6 hours
B. 8-10 hours
C. 24 hours
D. None. There is no standard or required TAT for consultation reports.

11. All of the following are true about report headings/subheadings *except*:

A. List subheadings vertically.
B. Change "diagnosis" to "diagnoses" when more than one diagnosis is provided.
C. Number all diagnoses even when there is only one provided.
D. Double-space between major sections of reports.

12. Which of the following type styles should *not* be used in transcription of medical records?

A. Bold type
B. Italics
C. Underlined type
D. All of the above

13. All of the following headings are typically found in an operative report *except*:

A. REVIEW OF SYSTEMS
B. ANESTHESIA

C. COMPLICATIONS
D. ESTIMATED BLOOD LOSS.

14. What typical turn-around time is established by most facilities for dictation of a discharge summary?

A. 24 hours
B. 5 days
C. 10 days
D. 30 days

15. Which of the following is *not* a report type included in the "Basic Four" acute care document types described in this chapter?

A. History and physical examination
B. Progress note
C. Operative report
D. Discharge summary

Proofreading/Editing

Correct the errors in each of the sentences below.

1. DIAGNOSIS
1. Urinary tract infection.

2. HEART: regular rate and rhythm.

3. ADMITTING DIAGNOSIS
1. Hypertension, uncontrolled.
2. Extreme fatigue.

4. DIAGNOSES
Coronary artery disease.

5. Stool culture was positive for *E. coli.*

6. Review of Systems: Normal except for sinus congestion for 2 days.

7. HPI: The patient is brought to the ER complaining of abdominal cramping and vaginal bleeding.

8. HEENT – Pupils are equal, round, and reactive to light.

9. SURGEON: John Edwards, MD.

10. Complications: None

Answer Key—Chapter 1

Refer to the answer keys below for answers to practical application exercises for this chapter.

Exam Prep Assessment

1. B
2. B
3. C
4. C
5. D
6. C
7. D
8. C
9. A
10. D
11. C
12. D
13. A
14. D
15. B

Proofreading/Editing

1. DIAGNOSIS
   Urinary tract infection.

2. HEART: Regular rate and rhythm.

3. ADMITTING DIAGNOSES
   1. Hypertension, uncontrolled.
   2. Extreme fatigue.

4. DIAGNOSIS
   Coronary artery disease.

5. Stool culture was positive for E coli.

6. REVIEW OF SYSTEMS: Normal except for sinus congestion for 2 days.

7. HISTORY OF PRESENT ILLNESS: The patient is brought to the ER complaining of abdominal cramping and vaginal bleeding.

8. HEENT: Pupils are equal, round, and reactive to light.

9. SURGEON: John Edwards, MD

10. COMPLICATIONS: None.

CHAPTER 2

Editing the Record

Learning objectives for this chapter:

- ✓ Understand and apply *Book of Style* (BOS) standards related to *when* and *how* an MT can reasonably and appropriately edit the medical record.
- ✓ Recognize transcription scenarios where it would *not* be appropriate for an MT to edit or modify the record.
- ✓ Know how to identify error/inconsistency in the record and notify/flag the report.
- ✓ Accurately identify these standards via multiple-choice questions that prepare you for AHDI credentialing examinations.

Introduction

While there is much debate in our industry about the risk management role of the MT and there are some environments where healthcare documentation specialists are required to capture "verbatim" dictation, most healthcare facilities and providers fully expect the MT to be engaged in proactive error analysis and recognition, correcting what falls within the scope of practice for the MT and flagging those inconsistencies that cannot be corrected by the MT. Until knowledge and experience frame the editorial boundaries of that scope of practice, as an MT, you should work in tandem with quality assurance coordinators and supervisors to ensure that you are editing (or not editing) to an appropriate degree. The value of the MT as an error recognition expert will only be more important as documentation moves into the EHR and MTs move out of traditional transcription and into editing roles.

Tips and Strategies for this Chapter:

- *Read the chapter thoroughly, highlighting or underlining terms and references that are unfamiliar to you.*
- *Read and be familiar with the Statement on Verbatim Transcription found in Appendix B of your BOS.*
- *Familiarize yourself with the chapter index found in the margin on the first page of this chapter in your BOS (page 23) and practice navigating the chapter using the index.*
- *Create two index cards, one for a list of "When to Edit" items and one for a list of "When Not to Edit" items that will help you set editorial boundaries for yourself as you acclimate to the transcription process.*

Exam Prep Assessment

Apply your understanding and knowledge of Chapter 2 to the multiple-choice exam prep questions below.

1. Which of these is an *acceptable* brief form?

   A. appy
   B. exam
   C. crit
   D. epi

2. An MT should edit all of the following *except*:

   A. syntax.
   B. spelling.
   C. back formations.
   D. direct quotes.

3. Which of the following is an example of a sentence that warrants editing by the MT?

   A. The wrist was x-rayed at the patient's request.
   B. The vertebra were within normal limits.

C. Bleeders were bovied and the wound reapproximated.
D. Stool cultures were sent to the lab.

4. For which of the following errors should an MT flag the report?

A. Unverifiable word or spelling
B. Slang terms
C. Transposition of values
D. Syntax errors

5. An MT should <u>not</u> edit:

A. punctuation errors.
B. wrong words.
C. missing dictation.
D. back formations.

6. Negative findings should be:

A. flagged to the attention of the dictator.
B. transcribed as dictated.
C. deleted or omitted.
D. None of the above.

7. Which of the following represents a sentence that warrants editing by the MT?

A. Sodium 4.2 and potassium 141.
B. Conjunctivae were red and inflamed.
C. There were no eos in the differential.
D. Hemoglobin was 20 and hematocrit 39.

8. ADT refers to ___________ data.

A. Assessment/Diagnosis/Treatment
B. Assessment/Discharge/Transfer
C. Admission/Diagnosis/Treatment
D. Admission/Discharge/Transfer

9. Which of the following is an example of an *acceptable* back formation?

   A. adhese
   B. diagnose
   C. pex
   D. cathed

10. The ability to mark the dictation file for quick access by QA personnel is called:

   A. dictation marking.
   B. dictation indexing.
   C. audio marking.
   D. audio indexing.

Proofreading/Editing

There are no proofreading/editing exercises for this chapter since the application of the editing guidelines covered here will be best applied to transcription examples and standards you will address in future chapters and in the transcription portion of your training.

Answer Key—Chapter 2

Refer to the answer key below for answers to the practical application exercise for this chapter.

Exam Prep Assessment

1. B
2. D
3. B
4. A
5. C
6. B
7. A
8. D
9. B
10. D

Record Privacy, Security, and Integrity

Learning objectives for this chapter:

- ✓ Understand and apply *Book of Style* (BOS) standards related to record privacy and security, including the HIPAA regulations, definitions, and compliance requirements unique to the healthcare documentation sector.
- ✓ Accurately identify these standards via multiple-choice questions that prepare you for AHDI credentialing examinations.

Introduction

Chapter 3 introduces the student/reader to the concept of privacy, security, and integrity of the legal medical record, outlining in detail how HIPAA has shaped business practices in the healthcare documentation sector, including how both in-house MT employees and at-home independent contractors are impacted by the privacy and security regulations. This chapter points out that business associates are not considered covered entities under the definition. However, since the publication of the 3rd edition *Book of Style*, the American Recovery and Reinvestment Act of 2009 (ARRA) made sweeping changes to the health information privacy and security regulations previously outlined by HIPAA. Business associates will be subject to civil and criminal penalties and enforcement proceedings for violations of HIPAA.

The definition of a business associate is also being expanded to include organizations that provide data transmission of protected health information to covered entities and business associates who require access on a routine basis to that protected health information. Examples of such organizations include health information exchange organizations, regional health information organizations, and vendors that contract with covered entities to provide personal health records. Transcriptionists working as independent contractors who enter into business associate agreements with provider clients should be aware that the privacy and security provisions of HIPAA now equally apply to them and not just to covered entities.

Tips and Strategies for this Chapter:

- *Read the chapter thoroughly, highlighting or underlining references that are unfamiliar to you, including acronyms and organizational names mentioned in this section.*
- *Highlight and/or make a list of all the guidelines in this chapter that will specifically relate to ensuring a HIPAA-compliant at-home office once you are working in the industry.*
- *Work in study groups to discuss potential scenarios where patient information might be knowingly or unknowingly disclosed and/or inappropriately accessed.*

Exam Prep Assessment

Apply your understanding and knowledge of Chapter 3 to the multiple-choice exam prep questions below.

1. HIPAA refers to the:

   A. Health Information Portability and Accessibility Act.
   B. Health Information Portability and Accountability Act.
   C. Health Insurance Portability and Accessibility Act.
   D. Health Insurance Portability and Accountability Act.

2. A covered entity or business associate may use or disclose PHI *without* the patient's consent to:

   A. make care decisions and provide treatment to the patient.
   B. request consent for surgery from the patient's insurance carrier.

C. submit bills for reimbursement of care.
D. All of the above.

3. PHI refers to:

A. patient health information.
B. protected health information.
C. patient health insurance.
D. protected health insurance.

4. Based on the HIPAA privacy rule definition, which of the following would *not* be considered a covered entity?

A. Cardiology clinic
B. Health insurance company
C. Transcription service organization
D. Outpatient surgery center

5. MTs who work as subcontractors are considered ____________________ under the HIPAA definition.

A. healthcare clearinghouses
B. covered entities
C. business associates
D. None of the above

6. The privacy rule requires that business associates agree to do all of the following *except:*

A. report to the patient any use or disclosure not permitted by the agreement.
B. ensure that subcontractors adhere to the same restrictions and conditions as business associates.
C. use appropriate safeguards to protect against unauthorized use or disclosure of the information.
D. destroy or return to the covered entity the protected health information once the agreement is terminated, if feasible.

7. According to HL7, a dictated addendum should be:

   A. added to the original document at the end of the report with a new signature line and date stamp.
   B. transcribed in a new document with its own document ID.
   C. added to the original document and incorporated into the body of the report above the original signature line.
   D. None of the above.

8. Which of the following stipulations must be met for a medical record to be admitted into a court of law under the hearsay exception?

   A. The record was made in the regular course of business.
   B. The entries in the record were made at or near the time the matter was recorded.
   C. The entries were made by the individual within the enterprise with firsthand knowledge of the acts, events, conditions, and opinions.
   D. All of the above.

9. According to ASTM E31, the signature line on an original document of an individual who has generated an amended document is called a/an:

   A. addendum signature.
   B. modification signature.
   C. administrative signature.
   D. error/edit signature.

10. The process by which the provider verifies what has been captured in the record and affixes his/her signature to the report is called:

    A. authentication.
    B. verification.
    C. affirmation.
    D. authorization.

11. Which of the following is recommended for secure electronic file transfer?

    A. 64-bit, random-algorithm encryption
    B. 64-bit, random-algorithm decryption

C. 128-bit, random-algorithm encryption
D. 128-bit, random-algorithm decryption

12. How often should the password on your computer be changed?

A. Every day
B. Once a week
C. Once a month
D. Every six months

13. Which of the following statements is *not* true when it comes to physical transport of patient records?

A. Use a trustworthy friend or colleague to transport patient records.
B. Use a service with tracking and recipient signature when shipping out of town.
C. Transport records in a sealed/locked and tamper-proof container.
D. Make sure no patient identifiable information is visible by the courier or third-party transport service.

14. Provision in a business associate contract whereby one party agrees to be financially responsible for specified types of damages, claims, and losses is called:

A. limitation of liability.
B. indemnification.
C. waiver of responsibility.
D. None of the above.

15. Which of the following is *not* a policy for record authentication as required by the Department of Health and Human Services?

A. All entries must be legible and complete.
B. Records can be authenticated by a provider representative or employee.
C. The author of each entry must be identified and must authenticate his/her entry.
D. Authentication may include signatures, written initials, or computer entry.

Proofreading/Editing

There are no proofreading/editing exercises for this chapter since the principles covered here relate to privacy and security and not to standards of style.

Answer Key—Chapter 3

Refer to the answer key below for answers to the practical application exercise for this chapter.

Exam Prep Assessment

1. A
2. D
3. B
4. C
5. D
6. A
7. B
8. D
9. B
10. A
11. C
12. C
13. A
14. B
15. B

CHAPTER 4

Grammar

Learning objectives for this chapter:

- ✓ Understand and apply *Book of Style* (BOS) standards related to parts of speech.
- ✓ Understand and apply *Book of Style* (BOS) standards related to parts of a sentence.
- ✓ Understand and apply *Book of Style* (BOS) standards related to parts of phrases and clauses.
- ✓ Understand and apply *Book of Style* (BOS) standards related to parts of sentence classification.
- ✓ Accurately identify these standards via multiple-choice questions that prepare you for AHDI credentialing examinations.

Introduction

Grammar refers to the set of rules governing a particular language. It is part of the overall study of language known as *linguistics*. Every language, whether formal or dialectical, has its own grammar—rules that govern the whys and hows of that language. While it may seem that grammar is only learned by formal instruction, the truth is that all languages have an inherent grammar that can be observed in a child long before that child enters "grammar school." Languages that arise in regions of blended ethnicity, for example, will naturally develop not only content but also a consistent pattern of grammar. For that reason, linguists often refer to *prescriptive* and *descriptive* grammars. Prescriptive grammars are those used by prestige groups within a language community, those that condemn the use of certain constructions that fall outside mainstream acceptability. Descriptive grammars represent the language that is actually used by people (e.g., the use of "ain't" or double negatives in speech). Modern linguists prefer descriptive grammar because it more accurately represents the way language is spoken and not the way a certain group or influence perceives that it *should* be spoken.

The business community, however, follows suit with the academic community in subscribing to prescriptive grammar in the English language in order to ensure consistency, standards, and clear communication. Healthcare documentation is no exception. The standard of expectation is that these records will reflect both accuracy and *quality*, the latter of which speaks to the grammatically correct expression of the healthcare information being outlined. It will be your responsibility as a medical transcriptionist to ensure that the record reflects that standard.

Tips and Strategies for this Chapter:

- *Read the chapter thoroughly, highlighting or underlining references that are unfamiliar to you, including unfamiliar parts of speech and grammatical terms.*
- *Make flashcards or note cards of the parts of speech, and types of sentences, phrases, and clauses—include examples of each on the back of your cards.*
- *Practice identifying these key parts of speech and phrase/clause types in sample clinical reports or the answer keys for your transcription module.*
- *Familiarize yourself with the chapter index found in the margin on the first page of this chapter in your BOS (page 57) and practice navigating the chapter using the index.*

Exam Prep Assessment

Apply your understanding and knowledge of Chapter 4 to the multiple-choice exam prep questions below.

1. Which of the following is an example of a *collective noun*?

   A. office
   B. colleague
   C. team
   D. unity

2. A pronoun combined with *–self* or *–selves* is called a/an ________________ pronoun.

   A. intensive
   B. reflexive
   C. relative
   D. personal

3. Which sentence contains a *relative pronoun*?

   A. He gave the shot to himself.
   B. To whom should I give my consent?
   C. That is a very good idea.
   D. Sue herself said it was necessary to make the call.

4. The word *nobody* is an example of a/an ____________________ pronoun.

   A. indefinite
   B. intensive
   C. interrogative
   D. demonstrative

5. The ____________________ receives the action of the verb or shows the result of an action.

   A. predicate nominative
   B. predicate adjective
   C. indirect object
   D. direct object

6. Which sentence contains a *participle*?

   A. I planned to take my test in May.
   B. Her only solace was her writing.
   C. Exam of the right lower leg revealed a red, weeping ulcerative lesion.
   D. He spent the summer helping his parents with their business.

7. Which is an example of a *compound-complex* sentence?

   A. She has no children, and her sister, who has a history of hypertension and breast CA, is her only living sibling.
   B. The patient presented with 3 days of nausea and vomiting and was admitted to the ER for rehydration and evaluation.
   C. Despite some initial objections to anesthesia, he ultimately agreed to the procedure.
   D. X-ray revealed scattered nodules in both lower lobes, confirming our original diagnosis.

8. Adverb clauses that contain missing words are called:

   A. subordinate clauses.
   B. simple clauses.
   C. elliptical clauses.
   D. descriptive clauses.

9. Identify the type of phrase or clause underlined in the following sentence:

   Thank you for referring Doris Smith, who presented to my office seeking evaluation for chronic back pain.

   A. prepositional phrase
   B. subordinate clause
   C. gerund phrase
   D. participial phrase

10. Which is an example of a *subordinating conjunction*?

    A. nor
    B. because
    C. among
    D. for

11. Which sentence contains a noun used as an adverb?

    A. Tomorrow is the day I get my test results back.
    B. She takes a daily dose of doxycycline for acne rosacea.

C. She called tonight looking for a refill of her pain medicine.
D. He will be seen in followup on Tuesday.

12. An adverb that is placed in such a way that it can be interpreted as modifying more than one word is called a/an ______________ modifier.

A. squinting
B. alternating
C. ambiguous
D. None of the above.

13. Verbs that express action without an object are called ______________ verbs.

A. transitive
B. intransitive
C. passive
D. helping

14. Which contains a *demonstrative* pronoun?

A. This plan was outlined in detail to the patient.
B. Anyone can improve heart health through exercise and proper diet.
C. She was given an anti-allergy medication that can safely be taken with her antihypertensive medications.
D. Whatever can be done will be done.

15. Which is an example of a *complex* sentence?

A. Walking heel to toe from one end of the room to the other, the patient showed no signs of neurologic deficit.
B. The patient, in a hurry to be discharged, left without formal instructions.
C. Palpation of the abdomen revealed exquisite tenderness along the lower edge of the liver.
D. A 12-lead EKG, which was transmitted en route via EMS, revealed significant ST depression.

Practical Application

Identify the part of speech or type of phrase/clause for each underlined item in the operative report excerpt below:

Under general endotracheal anesthesia[1], the patient was **placed**[2] in the left lateral decubitus position, and his right chest was prepped with Betadine and draped in a **sterile**[3] manner. A right lateral thoracotomy incision was made and carried **sharply**[4] through the subcutaneous tissues. We divided **the muscular layers**[5] with **electrocautery**[6]. The fifth interspace was identified **and**[7] the intercostal muscles divided. A section of the posterior fifth rib, **which was noted to have several healed fractures**[8], was resected. The chest spreader was placed and the chest explored. There was **one huge bulla**[9] of the right lower lobe, as well as two **moderate-sized**[10] bullae of the right lower lobe. **Using the TA-90 and TA-55 staplers**[11], the bullae were resected from the lower lobe. Using Ray-Tec sponges, pleurodesis was then carried out **over the entire pleural surface**[12]. **Two**[13] #32 chest tubes where then placed through separate incisions. The intercostal layers were closed with #2 Vicryl, the muscular layers were closed with **running**[14] 0 Vicryl, the subcutaneous layer was closed with running 3-0 Vicryl, and **the skin was closed with running 4-0 subcuticular Vicryl**[15].

Answer Key—Chapter 4

Refer to the answer keys below for answers to practical application exercises for this chapter.

Exam Prep Assessment

1. C
2. B
3. B
4. A

5. D
6. C
7. A
8. C
9. B
10. B
11. C
12. A
13. B
14. A
15. D

Practical Application

1. Prepositional phrase
2. Verb (intransitive)
3. Adjective
4. Adverb
5. Direct object
6. Noun
7. Coordinating conjunction
8. Dependent (subordinate) clause
9. Predicate nominative
10. Adjective (compound modifier)
11. Participial phrase
12. Prepositional phrase
13. Adjective
14. Participle
15. Independent clause

Usage

Learning objectives for this chapter:

- ✓ Understand and apply *Book of Style* (BOS) standards related to verb and pronoun usage.
- ✓ Understand and apply *Book of Style* (BOS) standards related to subject/verb agreement.
- ✓ Understand and apply *Book of Style* (BOS) standards related to pronoun and antecedent agreement.
- ✓ Accurately identify these standards via multiple-choice questions that prepare you for AHDI credentialing examinations.
- ✓ Apply your knowledge of these standards to proofreading/editing exercises that prepare you for practical application in the workplace and on AHDI credentialing examinations.

Introduction

Usage is a complex and entertaining domain in the arena of language. It involves the address of "rights" and "wrongs" in how people use language, a practice that is inarguably subjective when you consider that language evolves from different sources and dialects, and what may seem a correct expression to one may be wholly unacceptable to another. Usage "errors" can often be divided into two categories—those that deviate from the standard due to regional acceptance and those that are wrong regardless of region or dialect. For example, a Southerner will consider it quite acceptable to say, "Look what the cat drug in," where the use of "dragged" would be considered standard usage elsewhere. However, such faux pas in diction as "for all intensive purposes" or "bode of confidence" are just plain wrong regardless of region or dialect. If we were to leave the subject of usage in the hands of the user, we would have very few standards to guide us. In professional writing, legal discourse, and formal communication, conformity with standard English is expected, and medical transcriptionists should pay close attention to the rules for agreement and diction that govern formal communication, as the MT is apt to hear all manner of usage errors and variances in the course of dictation.

Tips and Strategies for this Chapter:

- *Read the chapter thoroughly, highlighting or underlining references that are unfamiliar to you, including definitions for tenses and pronoun cases that are new or need review.*
- *Make flashcards or note cards of the key elements of this chapter—include examples of each on the back of your cards.*
- *Familiarize yourself with the chapter index found in the margin on the first page of this chapter in your BOS (page 81) and practice navigating the chapter using the index.*

Exam Prep Assessment

Apply your understanding and knowledge of Chapter 5 to the multiple-choice exam prep questions below.

1. Which of the following refers to *word choice*?

   A. tense
   B. mood
   C. diction
   D. agreement

2. Which is transcribed correctly?

   A. There is a high number of suicides reported each year in that region.
   B. Each group were taken on the tour of the facility.

C. The number of medications she is taking is noted in the chart.
D. The mumps are rarely seen in childhood these days due to successful immunization practices.

3. The indefinite pronoun *either* is:

    A. always singular.
    B. always plural.
    C. singular or plural depending on the noun it refers to.
    D. None of the above.

4. The ________________ mood makes requests or demands.

    A. indicative
    B. imperative
    C. subjunctive
    D. superlative

5. Which represents a correct expression of agreement?

    A. Her family history, but not her other risk factors, are worrisome for heart disease.
    B. Adequate surgical prep, including Betadine scrub and sterile draping, were accomplished.
    C. The compelling nature of the acidosis, not the presence of a presumed toxin, was felt to be the diagnostic indicator.
    D. Most of the team are attending the conference being held across the street.

6. The ________________ tense is used to express action completed in the past before some other past action or event.

    A. historic present
    B. past perfect
    C. present perfect
    D. past

7. Each sentence below is expressed in passive voice *except:*

    A. The patient tolerated the procedure well.
    B. No prominent abnormal lymphocyte population is identified.
    C. Received is one alcohol-fixed smear.
    D. The patient's chest was prepped and draped in the usual sterile manner.

8. Which noun has the same form in the plural and the singular?

    A. credentials
    B. odds
    C. assets
    D. series

9. Which is transcribed correctly?

    A. The United Nations have issued a statement on the issue of global poverty.
    B. Approximately 5 mL of cloudy urine were extracted from the bladder during autopsy.
    C. Lidocaine with epinephrine 1:100,000 was instilled into the identified space.
    D. Here is a number of reasons to consider smoking cessation.

10. A pronoun must agree with its antecedent in:

    A. person, place, and number.
    B. number, gender, and person.
    C. person, place, and gender.
    D. gender, place, and number.

11. Which is not the correct expression of a pronoun whose gender is unknown or whose antecedent represents both genders?

    A. A medical transcriptionist should apply his/her informed judgment to the documentation process.
    B. Medical transcriptionists should apply their informed judgment to the documentation process.
    C. Medical transcriptionists should apply informed judgment to the documentation process.

D. A medical transcriptionist should apply her informed judgment to the documentation process.

12. Which is an example of an inverted sentence?

   A. Enclosed is a copy of the patient's last EKG.
   B. Take these prescriptions downstairs to the pharmacy on the first floor.
   C. Atropine was administered without change on the monitor.
   D. Attached to the chart, the patient's medication list revealed several anti-hypertensive medications.

13. A pronoun that acts as the subject is in the ____________________ case.

   A. objective
   B. subjective
   C. nominative
   D. None of the above

14. All of the following represent correct subject-verb agreement *except:*

   A. Neither the x-rays nor her lab results are consistent with a rheumatoid diagnosis.
   B. I suspect that either her old glasses or work-related stress is causing her frequent headaches.
   C. Not only massage but also acupuncture are recommended for alternative intervention.
   D. It is apparent that the patient's spouse or children have been advising her about hospice care.

15. Which is expressed in the *past perfect tense*?

   A. The patient works for the city of Miami.
   B. Apparently, he had been taking over-the-counter glucosamine for his shoulder pain.
   C. She is telling me that she cannot tolerate the anti-inflammatory medication she was previously prescribed.
   D. When he receives his new insurance card, he will bring a copy to the office.

Proofreading/Editing

Correct the errors in each of the sentences below.

1. The number of swine flu cases in our area are reportedly now in the hundreds.
2. Either the shoes she's been wearing at work or the change in how many hours she spends standing up have made a difference in her plantar fasciitis.
3. This series of x-rays show significant worsening of her degenerative disease.
4. Adhered to the anterior surfaces of both the 9th and 10th ribs were a significant amount of post-surgical scar tissue.
5. The Northwest Council of Presidents held their meeting in Portland this year.
6. Fever for the last three days and a long history of urinary tract infections are the reason she presents to my office today.
7. Every tubal ligation patient is counseled about their desire for future pregnancies.
8. Some of her symptoms appears to be psychosomatic.
9. The assisted living facility, but not her family members, believe the patient is depressed.
10. The logistics of implementing her treatment plan needs to be worked out.

Answer Key—Chapter 5

Refer to the answer keys below for answers to practical application exercises for this chapter.

Exam Prep Assessment

1. C
2. C
3. A
4. B
5. C
6. B

7. A
8. D
9. C
10. B
11. D
12. A
13. C
14. C
15. B

Proofreading/Editing

1. The number of swine flu cases in our area is reportedly now in the hundreds.
2. Either the shoes she's been wearing at work or the change in how many hours she spends standing up has made a difference in her plantar fasciitis.
3. This series of x-rays shows significant worsening of her degenerative disease.
4. Adhered to the anterior surfaces of both the 9th and 10th ribs was a significant amount of post-surgical scar tissue.
5. The Northwest Council of Presidents held its meeting in Portland this year.
6. Fever for the last three days and a long history of urinary tract infections are the reasons she presents to my office today.
7. Every tubal ligation patient is counseled about her desire for future pregnancies.
8. Some of her symptoms appear to be psychosomatic.
9. The assisted living facility, but not her family members, believes the patient is depressed.
10. The logistics of implementing her treatment plan need to be worked out.

CHAPTER 6

Punctuation

Learning objectives for this chapter:

- ✓ Understand and apply *Book of Style* (BOS) standards related to all forms of punctuation, particularly the complex rules for comma placement to separate and to set off.
- ✓ Accurately identify these standards via multiple-choice questions that prepare you for AHDI credentialing examinations.
- ✓ Apply your knowledge of these standards to proofreading/editing exercises that prepare you for practical application in the workplace and on AHDI credentialing examinations.

Introduction

Punctuation marks serve a vital role in sentence construction. They are relationship indicators when word order alone is not sufficient to convey meaning. Without major punctuation, there would be no visual boundaries around the written word to guide the reader from one concept, or idea, to the next. Without punctuation, documentation would be a visual mess.

As a medical transcriptionist, you will be tasked with accurately punctuating the sentences dictated to you; the knack of incorporating this into the natural flow of your transcription will develop over time. This area of transcription can be particularly frustrating to the MT, since physicians do not always dictate sentence flow in a manner that facilitates clean punctuation, and many will attempt to dictate punctuation where it should not be placed.

This is one of the few areas in the report where MTs are encouraged *not* to rely on physician direction. As with spelling, physicians cannot always be relied upon to provide accurate direction with documentation. Many will attempt to dictate punctuation as part of the report. Occasionally, you will encounter a dictator who possesses the language skills that might make this helpful. However, this is not always the case. A physician, whose primary skill set lies in the clinical arena, cannot be relied upon to have advanced writing skills, and it is the MT's responsibility to ensure that punctuation is judiciously applied to the patient record.

Knowledge of punctuation rules and a very clear understanding of applying these rules will be essential to producing a quality document. An MT who is relying on a vague or "general" understanding of punctuation will encounter difficulty in this area. For example, some people are under the mistaken impression that commas should be placed anywhere that you "pause" in the sentence. An MT will quickly discover that this rule is impossible to apply to dictation that is delivered by providers who either chronically pause throughout their dictation or *never* pause from the moment they begin a report until they sign off from it.

There are many clear rules governing the placement of punctuation in formal writing. MTs should avoid the random and haphazard placement of punctuation, particularly commas, and begin to develop a substantive ability to analyze sentences; determine the role and function of the words, phrases, and clauses within those sentences; and apply punctuation therein with informed confidence.

Tips and Strategies for this Chapter:

- *Read the chapter thoroughly, highlighting or underlining references that are unfamiliar to you, paying particular attention to highlighted examples demonstrating inclusion and omission of key punctuation marks.*
- *Practice identifying the placement or omission of punctuation marks, especially commas, in sample clinical reports or the answer keys for your transcription module, providing standards-driven rationale for each omission and inclusion to help you better understand the <u>why</u> behind placement of commas in written language.*
- *Familiarize yourself with the chapter index found in the margin on the first page of this chapter in your BOS (pages 103-104) and practice navigating the chapter using the index.*

Exam Prep Assessment

Apply your understanding and knowledge of Chapter 6 to the multiple-choice exam prep questions below.

1. Use a period:

   A. at the end of a direct question.
   B. after numbers in an enumerated list when they are enclosed in parentheses.
   C. with lowercased abbreviations and acronyms.
   D. with abbreviated metric units of measure.

2. Which represents correct use of quotation marks?

   A. Did he say he "needed his pain medication"?
   B. He is a well-developed, well-nourished male standing 6′2″ tall.
   C. The patient complained of a "funny feeling" in her legs.
   D. All of the above.

3. A *suspensive* hyphen is used correctly in which of these sentences?

   A. She complained of 4- to 6-weeks of intermittent headaches.
   B. She complained of a 4-6 week history of intermittent headaches.
   C. She complained of 4-to-6 weeks of intermittent headaches.
   D. She complained of a 4- to 6-week history of intermittent headaches.

4. Use a question mark:

   A. at the end of an indirect question.
   B. at the end of a direct question.
   C. when the physician dictates "questionable" in relation to the diagnosis.
   D. All of the above.

5. A *separating* comma is needed in which of the following sentences?

   A. Despite having 9/10 pain on arrival to the ER the patient refused medication for pain.
   B. This 52-year-old black male presented to my office for consultation.

C. Initial laboratory workup revealed a WBC of 2200.
D. Today we will get a CBC before she leaves the office.

6. Use commas to separate:

A. laboratory values of a single panel or test.
B. direct dialogue from the rest of the sentence.
C. chromosome number and sex chromosome in a genetic expression.
D. All of the above.

7. Which is correct?

A. Her time on the treadmill was 13-minutes, 43-seconds.
B. Her time on the treadmill was 13 minutes 43 seconds.
C. Her time on the treadmill was 13 minutes, 43 seconds.
D. Her time on the treadmill was 13-minutes 43-seconds.

8. All of these are conditions for using a hyphen in a range expression *except*:

A. Decimals and/or commas do not appear in the numeric values.
B. Neither value is accompanied by a symbol.
C. Neither value contains three or more digits.
D. Neither value is a negative.

9. Which is a correct fractional expression?

A. 3-1/2 feet
B. one fourth completed
C. 6 1/4 inches
D. 2-1/2-pounds

10. Use a virgule (/) for the word *per* when:

A. the construction involves at least one English unit of measure.
B. at least one element includes a specific numeric quantity.
C. at least one element includes a fractional expression.
D. None of the above.

11. Which is transcribed correctly?

    A. The patient says she has been compliant with her medications, however her husband questions this.
    B. The patient says she has been compliant with her medications, however, her husband questions this.
    C. The patient says she has been compliant with her medications; however her husband questions this.
    D. The patient says she has been compliant with her medications; however, her husband questions this.

12. All of the following are correct expressions of a compound modifier *except*:

    A. up-to-date immunizations.
    B. doctor-patient relationship.
    C. lovely sounding voice.
    D. severly damaged tissue.

13. Which of the following is punctuated correctly?

    A. The patient was brought to the OR, and after being placed in the dorsal lithotomy position, was prepped and draped in the usual sterile fashion.
    B. The patient was brought to the OR, and, after being placed in the dorsal lithotomy position, was prepped and draped in the usual sterile fashion.
    C. The patient was brought to the OR and after being placed in the dorsal lithotomy position was prepped and draped in the usual sterile fashion.
    D. The patient was brought to the OR and after being placed in the dorsal lithotomy position, was prepped and draped in the usual sterile fashion.

14. A hyphen is used appropriately in all of the following *except*:

    A. There was a jagged, 3-inch laceration on the anterior calf that required reapproximation and closure in the ER.
    B. She progressed rapidly through end-stage labor and delivered a healthy baby boy weighing 7-pounds 4-ounces.
    C. There was a well-circumscribed nodular lesion on her right upper arm with a 1.5 cm diameter.
    D. He described his work over the weekend as "back-breaking."

15. Which eponym is expressed correctly?

   A. Right and left Jackson Pratt drains were placed to assist with postoperative drainage.
   B. Her past medical history is significant for diagnosis with Epstein Barr virus during her sophomore year in college.
   C. EMS report indicates that the patient was unresponsive and exhibiting Cheyne-Stokes breathing when rescue arrived.
   D. The patient was taken to the OR with non-pathological intracapsular femoral neck fracture for Austin-Moore hemiarthroplasty.

Proofreading/Editing

Correct the punctuation errors in each of the sentences below.

1. She has right sided hemiparesis, atrial fibrillation and diabetes.

2. After eating oysters at a party 2 days ago she began to have bowel distention and this has rapidly increased today.

3. Examination of the left lower extremity reveals 1+ swelling, however, there is no dependent edema present on examination.

4. Because he became combative, violent and abusive Security had to be involved in subduing the patient and haloperidol 5 mg and Ativan 2 mg IM was used to help control the patient.

5. RECOMMENDATION: Hydration analgesia and observation, and if stone does not pass within 72 hours [or less], I would recommend the patient for ureteroscopy stone-basketing and ultrasonic lithotripsy.

6. She was found to have a sebaceous cyst that on the surface of the back appeared to be slightly less than 2-cm in diameter but, after incision and excavation, it was found to have a subcutaneous diameter of nearly 8 cm.

7. When asked if she had a history of drug abuse she replied "Are you kidding"?

8. Because of heavy bleeding, that has repeatedly decreased the hematocrit to the 26% to 28% range, and which interferes with her quality of life and ability to work, the patient has requested TAH which will be carried out at this time.

9. At the present time there is no nodule irregularity or active lesion and the biopsy site is well healed.

10. On her previous visit the patient was given multiple options for managing her chronic plantar fasciitis such as custom shoe inserts to be worn while working on her feet, which she states she has just started wearing, exercises to strengthen the plantar fascia, and wearing night splints to keep the fascia extended, which she says she tried to do for several nights but could not tolerate their weight and bulk while sleeping.

Answer Key—Chapter 6

Refer to the answer keys below for answers to practical application exercises for this chapter.

Exam Prep Assessment

1. C
2. C
3. D
4. B
5. A
6. D
7. B
8. C
9. A
10. B
11. D
12. C
13. C
14. B
15. C

Proofreading/Editing

1. She has right-sided hemiparesis, atrial fibrillation, and diabetes. *(Comma optional but preferred after "fibrillation")*

2. After eating oysters at a party 2 days ago, she began to have bowel distention, and this has rapidly increased today.

3. Examination of the left lower extremity reveals 1+ swelling; however, there is no dependent edema present on examination.

4. Because he became combative, violent, and abusive, Security had to be involved in subduing the patient, and haloperidol 5 mg and Ativan 2 mg IM was used to help control the patient. *(Comma optional but preferred after "violent")*

5. RECOMMENDATION: Hydration, analgesia, and observation, and if stone does not pass within 72 hours (or less), I would recommend the patient for ureteroscopy, stone-basketing, and ultrasonic lithotripsy. *(Commas optional but preferred after "analgesia" and "stone-basketing")*

6. She was found to have a sebaceous cyst that on the surface of the back appeared to be slightly less than 2 cm in diameter, but after incision and excavation, it was found to have a subcutaneous diameter of nearly 8 cm.

7. When asked if she had a history of drug abuse, she replied, "Are you kidding?"

8. Because of heavy bleeding that has repeatedly decreased the hematocrit to the 26% to 28% range and which interferes with her quality of life and ability to work, the patient has requested TAH, which will be carried out at this time.

9. At the present time there is no nodule irregularity or active lesion, and the biopsy site is well healed.

10. On her previous visit the patient was given multiple options for managing her chronic plantar fasciitis such as custom shoe inserts to be worn while working on her feet, which she states she has just started wearing; exercises to strengthen the plantar fascia; and wearing night splints to keep the fascia extended, which she says she tried to do for several nights but could not tolerate their weight and bulk while sleeping.

Transcription Practice

Complete the Transcription Practice exercises for Chapter 6 on the CD-ROM included with this text. Answers to these exercises can be found in Appendix A at the back of this book.

CHAPTER 7

Capitalization

Learning objectives for this chapter:

- ✓ Understand and apply *Book of Style* (BOS) standards related to capitalization.
- ✓ Accurately identify these standards via multiple-choice questions that prepare you for AHDI credentialing examinations.
- ✓ Apply your knowledge of these standards to proofreading/editing exercises that prepare you for practical application in the workplace and on AHDI credentialing examinations.

Introduction

Capitals emphasize and draw attention to the terms in which they are used. Use them appropriately and judiciously because their overuse diminishes their value and impact.Some words are always capitalized, some never. The placement or use of a term may determine whether it is capitalized. Capitals, for example, are always used to mark the beginning of a sentence.

Learning and adopting the rules of capitalization, when they should be used and when they should not be used, as well as the few instances when variations may be acceptable, will improve the consistency, accuracy, and communication value of transcribed healthcare documents.

In particular, avoid the use of unnecessary or inappropriate capitals, whether that means capitalizing a clinical specialty, family title, or academic degree (especially when they are used in the general sense) or capitalizing all drugs rather than being mindful of the need to delineate a brand drug from a generic.

Tips and Strategies for this Chapter:

- *Read the chapter thoroughly, highlighting or underlining references that are unfamiliar to you.*
- *Make two index cards or lists for reference, labeling one "Always capitalize" and the other "Never Capitalize." Include a list of rules and exceptions under each label for quick reference while you transcribe.*
- *Familiarize yourself with the chapter index found in the margin on the first page of this chapter in your BOS (page 145) and practice navigating the chapter using the index.*

Exam Prep Assessment

Apply your understanding and knowledge of Chapter 7 to the multiple-choice exam prep questions below.

1. Capitalize the first word after a colon *if:*

    A. the material that follows is subordinate and cannot stand alone as a sentence.
    B. it is a proper noun or other word that is automatically capitalized.
    C. it is the first word of a dependent clause used to express special emphasis.
    D. the material that follows represents a formal rule or instruction.

2. Each of these is capitalized correctly *except:*

    A. War And Peace.
    B. Explanation of Benefits form.
    C. German.
    D. Grade 2.

3. Which is correct?

    A. Discharge instructions were given in detail to mom and dad.
    B. She was brought to the emergency room by her Aunt, who doesn't speak any English and cannot provide reliable history.
    C. I spent a great deal of time with the mom outlining the course of treatment for her son's disease.
    D. Apparently, she works for her Uncle.

4. Capitalize an official title when:

   A. it is used in direct address.
   B. the personal name that follows it is an appositive.
   C. it follows a personal name.
   D. it is used in place of a personal name.

5. Which of the following eponymous terms is expressed correctly?

   A. Alzheimer Disease
   B. Ligament of Treitz
   C. Gram-positive rods
   D. parkinsonian tremors

6. Which sentence contains a correctly capitalized organization term?

   A. She was scheduled for KUB, but X-ray sent her back because she refused the study.
   B. The lesion was carefully dissected and sent for Pathology.
   C. She was seen in Cardiology consult and scheduled for angioplasty.
   D. The Pathology came back showing early dedifferentiation.

7. All of these drugs are expressed correctly *except:*

   A. acetaminophen.
   B. St. John's Wort.
   C. doxycycline.
   D. Ambien.

8. Assigning human qualities, actions, or characteristics to a place or a thing is called:

   A. personalization.
   B. humanization.
   C. personification.
   D. characterization.

9. Which of these should *not* be capitalized?

    A. Escape key
    B. HITECH Act
    C. Caucasian
    D. Baptism

10. Always capitalize:

    A. the names of seasons.
    B. compass points.
    C. medals and honors.
    D. holidays.

11. Which is transcribed correctly?

    A. We reviewed these routine preoperative instructions with her: stop taking the anti-inflammatory 10 days prior to surgery and avoid eating or drinking anything after midnight the night before surgery.
    B. We reviewed these routine preoperative instructions with her: Stop taking the anti-inflammatory 10 days prior to surgery and avoid eating or drinking anything after midnight the night before surgery.
    C. We reviewed these routine preoperative instructions with her: 1) stop taking the anti-inflammatory 10 days prior to surgery and 2) avoid eating or drinking anything after midnight the night before surgery.
    D. All of the above.

12. Genus names should be capitalized when:

    A. used in the plural form.
    B. used in the adjectival form.
    C. they stand alone.
    D. they are accompanied by a species name.

13. All of the following are expressed correctly *except:*

    A. Actinobacillus capsulatus.
    B. C difficile.

C. Strep pneumonia.
D. Streptococcus pneumoniae.

14. Which of the following contains a reference that should *not* be capitalized?

A. 34-year-old Asian female
B. New York City
C. The Lincoln Memorial
D. Pacific Basin

15. Which program or concept is capitalized correctly?

A. Socialist Reform
B. New Age Movement
C. Conservative ideology
D. Communist manifesto

Proofreading/Editing

Correct the capitalization errors in each of the sentences below.

1. The patient was combative on examination, kicking and yelling "leave me alone" when I tried to evaluate her.
2. She was transferred to the Postsurgical Care Unit.
3. He was diagnosed with Rocky Mountain Spotted Fever in his early 20s.
4. She admits to smoking a pack and a half a day (She has apparently tried to quit twice.) and drinks occasionally.
5. She saw Dr. Clark originally for her Von Willebrand disease, but she is presently under Dr. Smith's management for this.
6. Her culture grew out group-B Streptococcus.
7. This is a 32-year-old White male in no acute distress.
8. He has worked for the city of Jacksonville for 13 years.

9. She was given rhogam after her first pregnancy.

10. Does this say "take twice a day?"

Answer Key—Chapter 7

Refer to the answer keys below for answers to practical application exercises for this chapter.

Exam Prep Assessment

1. B
2. A
3. C
4. A
5. D
6. A
7. B
8. C
9. D
10. D
11. B
12. D
13. C
14. C
15. B

Proofreading/Editing

1. The patient was combative on examination, kicking and yelling "Leave me alone!" when I tried to evaluate her.
2. She was transferred to the postsurgical care unit.
3. He was diagnosed with Rocky Mountain spotted fever in his early 20s.
4. She admits to smoking a pack and a half a day (she has apparently tried to quit twice) and drinks occasionally.
5. She saw Dr. Clark originally for her von Willebrand disease, but she is presently under Dr. Smith's management for this.

6. Her culture grew out group-B streptococcus.

7. This is a 32-year-old white male in no acute distress.

8. He has worked for the City of Jacksonville for 13 years.

9. She was given Rhogam after her first pregnancy.

10. Does this say "Take twice a day"?

Transcription Practice

Complete the Transcription Practice exercises for Chapter 7 on the CD-ROM included with this text. Answers to these exercises can be found in Appendix A at the back of this book.

Plurals and Possessives

Learning objectives for this chapter:

- ✓ Understand and apply *Book of Style* (BOS) standards related to pluralization, including plural forms of both English and foreign terms, abbreviations, numbers, and symbols.
- ✓ Understand and apply *Book of Style* (BOS) standards related to demonstrating possession, including possessive forms of both English and foreign terms, abbreviations, numbers, and symbols.
- ✓ Accurately identify these standards via multiple-choice questions that prepare you for AHDI credentialing examinations.
- ✓ Apply your knowledge of these standards to proofreading/editing exercises that prepare you for practical application in the workplace and on AHDI credentialing examinations.
- ✓ Apply your knowledge of these standards in a simulated work setting through transcription of sample dictation clips designed to test the standards outlined in this chapter.

Introduction

Nowhere in language is there a greater hodgepodge of conflicting standards and rules than in the area of pluralization. Any attempt to memorize hard-and-fast rules can yield great frustration, for as soon as we've learned a rule, we discover all of its pesky contradictions and exceptions. For example, if the plural of *box* is *boxes* and *fox* is *foxes*, shouldn't the plural of *ox* be *oxes*? And if more than one *goose* is described as *geese*, why is the plural of *noose* not *neese* or *moose* not *meese?* We see this conundrum even in the pluralization of foreign terms, where there are always some notable exceptions. Words ending in *–is* are pluralized by changing *–is* to *–es*, but *arthritis* becomes the oddly formed *arthritides*. A transcriptionist has to be on his or her proverbial toes to stay ahead of the curve balls encountered in any address of appropriate plurals.

Possessives are more straightforward. The placement of an apostrophe (either alone or with an *–s*) serves in almost every case to identify the plural case of an English noun, and the exceptions are few. Where the possessive form of compounds is concerned, the MT has to be slightly more careful to think critically because the combination of a plural *and* possessive in relation to compound forms can get confusing. Beyond that, possessive forms lack the confusing complexity found in other areas of grammar.

Tips and Strategies for this Chapter:

- *Read the chapter thoroughly, highlighting or underlining references that are unfamiliar to you.*
- *Make index cards for the foreign plurals, which typically represent unfamiliar territory for a student or new MT, including examples and exceptions on the back of the card.*
- *Practice making plurals of clinical terms and foreign words by extracting nouns from your transcript keys and/or sample reports and making them either plural or singular based on the form used in the report.*
- *For possessives, make two lists or index cards. Make a list of all instances that plurals require an apostrophe plus –s and a list of all the plurals that take an apostrophe alone. Refer to this as you transcribe.*
- *Familiarize yourself with the chapter index found in the margin on the first page of this chapter in your BOS (page 169) and practice navigating the chapter using the index.*

Exam Prep Assessment

Apply your understanding and knowledge of Chapter 8 to the multiple-choice exam prep questions below.

1. Which sentence reflects accurate expression of an eponym?

   A. His Apgar's were 8 and 10 at one and five minutes.
   B. We discussed the long-term outlook of her non-Hodgkin's lymphoma.
   C. His family history is significant for a brother with Lou Gehrig's.
   D. Tinel's sign was negative.

2. Which of these is expressed correctly?

   A. sister-in-laws recipe
   B. sisters-in-law's recipes
   C. sisters-in-laws recipe
   D. sister-in-laws' recipes

3. Add –*s* to pluralize:

   A. double-digit numbers expressed as figures.
   B. brief forms.
   C. upper case abbreviations.
   D. All of the above.

4. Which is <u>*not*</u> a correctly pluralized abbreviation?

   A. lbs
   B. dcL
   C. rbc's
   D. EKGs

5. Add –*es* to pluralize words ending in:

   A. *"o"* preceded by a vowel.
   B. *"y"* preceded by a vowel.
   C. *"s," "x," "ch," "sh,"* or *"z."*
   D. *"f"* or *"ef."*

6. Which noun below would be classified as an irregular plural form?

   A. leaves
   B. tomatoes
   C. mice
   D. faxes

7. Each of these is always singular *except*:

   A. ascites.
   B. biceps.
   C. lues.
   D. genetics.

8. Form the plural of compounds ending in *–ful* by:

   A. adding *–s.*
   B. adding *–es.*
   C. adding an apostrophe and *–s.*
   D. None of the above.

9. Which is correctly pluralized?

   A. Blood sugars have been running in the 80's range.
   B. She had tubal ligation in her early 30s.
   C. EKG showed inverted Ts.
   D. He scored two 9s on Apgars and weighed 8 pounds 8 ounces.

10. Latin terms ending in *–a* should be pluralized by:

    A. adding *–e.*
    B. changing *–a* to *–us.*
    C. changing *–a* to *–on.*
    D. changing *–a* to *–um.*

11. Which is a correct singular form?

    A. ossa coxae
    B. nuclei polposi

C. placenta previa
D. verrucae vulgares

12. All of these are pluralized correctly *except*:

    A. diaphyses.
    B. stretococci.
    C. meati.
    D. thrombi.

13. The plural form of *diverticulum*:

    A. diverticula.
    B. diverticulas.
    C. diverticuli.
    D. diverticulae.

14. Which is correct?

    A. DIAGNOSIS: Bilateral pneumoniae.
    B. Past history is significant for bilateral carpal tunnel releases.
    C. There were plantar warts on her bilateral feet.
    D. OPERATION: Bilateral lumpectomy.

15. Which noun below would require an apostrophe and –*s* to show possession?

    A. pliers
    B. class
    C. Miss Graves
    D. forceps

Proofreading/Editing

Correct the pluralization and possessive errors in each of the sentences below.

1. X-rays of the cervical spine showed cervical spondylosis with encroachment on the neural foramen of C5 and C6.

2. The breasts contained no masses and axilla are free of nodes.

3. He was diagnosed with idiopathic dilated cardiomyopathy in his early 30's.

4. The patient sustained a left tricep tear on two separate occasions as a result of aggressive weight-lifting.

5. She had a positive Homan's sign but absence of any other diagnostic evidence conclusive for DVT.

6. HEENT: Sclera anicteric; conjunctiva clear.

7. She has been taking 2 teaspoonsful of cough medicine, which she says did little to resolve her nocturnal fits of coughing.

8. DIAGNOSIS: Patent ductus arteriosis.

9. DIAGNOSIS
   1. Status post myocardial infarction.
   2. Uncontrolled hypertension.

10. Examination of the transverse colon revealed multiple inflamed diverticuli.

Answer Key—Chapter 8

Refer to the answer keys below for answers to practical application exercises for this chapter.

Exam Prep Assessment

1. C
2. B
3. D
4. A
5. C
6. C
7. B
8. A
9. B
10. A
11. C
12. C

13. A

14. B

15. B

Proofreading/Editing

1. X-rays of the cervical spine showed cervical spondylosis with encroachment on the neural foramina of C5 and C6.

2. The breasts contained no masses and axillae are free of nodes.

3. He was diagnosed with idiopathic dilated cardiomyopathy in his early 30s.

4. The patient sustained a left triceps tear on two separate occasions as a result of aggressive weight-lifting.

5. She had a positive Homans sign but absence of any other diagnostic evidence conclusive for DVT.

6. HEENT: Sclerae anicteric; conjunctivae clear.

7. She has been taking 2 teaspoonfuls of cough medicine, which she says did little to resolve her nocturnal fits of coughing.

8. DIAGNOSIS: Patent ductus arteriosus.

9. DIAGNOSES
   1. Status post myocardial infarction.
   2. Uncontrolled hypertension.

10. Examination of the transverse colon revealed multiple inflamed diverticula.

Transcription Practice

Complete the Transcription Practice exercises for Chapter 8 on the CD-ROM included with this text. Answers to these exercises can be found in Appendix A at the back of this book.

CHAPTER 9

Abbreviations

Learning objectives for this chapter:

- ✓ Understand and apply *Book of Style* (BOS) standards related to abbreviations, including general rules for retention and expansion in a health record setting.
- ✓ Understand and apply *Book of Style* (BOS) standards related to *dangerous* abbreviations, as defined by organizations such as the Joint Commission and ISMP, including when and how to address identified abbreviations in a transcription setting.
- ✓ Accurately identify these standards via multiple-choice questions that prepare you for AHDI credentialing examinations.
- ✓ Apply your knowledge of these standards to proofreading/editing exercises that prepare you for practical application in the workplace and on AHDI credentialing examinations.
- ✓ Apply your knowledge of these standards in a simulated work setting through transcription of sample dictation clips designed to test the standards outlined in this chapter.

Introduction

Ultimately, the application of abbreviation standards comes down to some fundamental common-sense principles. The objective, as is the case with most standards of style and expression, is to promote clarity in the healthcare record. An abbreviated form, when used, should meet this objective, and the application of capitalization or the use of punctuation to indicate plurality or possession of an abbreviation should likewise promote clarity and be used consistently throughout the healthcare record. Of course, the overall goal of these standards is to encourage their consistent use across the entire healthcare delivery system.

Although some standards in this text do not have a significant impact on patient outcomes, the ones associated with dangerous abbreviations _do_. These abbreviations have been deemed dangerous by authorities who evaluate risk management and patient safety, and every member of the healthcare team, from provider to transcriptionist, needs to be aware of them. Many providers will continue to dictate the dangerous forms out of habit, and the responsibility for recognizing them and either flagging them to the attention of the physician or editing them appropriately will fall on the shoulders of the alert MT.

Tips and Strategies for this Chapter:

- *Read the chapter thoroughly, highlighting or underlining references that are unfamiliar to you.*
- *Make index cards of all the dangerous abbreviations, separating them out by those on the minimum list, those on the remainder of the Joint Commission's list, and those on the ISMP list.*
- *Familiarize yourself with the chapter index found in the margin on the first page of this chapter in your BOS (page 193) and practice navigating the chapter using the index.*

Exam Prep Assessment

Apply your understanding and knowledge of Chapter 9 to the multiple-choice exam prep questions below.

1. Which of the following is _not_ on the ISMP list as a dangerous abbreviation?

   A. HCl
   B. q.h.s.
   C. mL
   D. cc

2. All of these are acceptable expressions *except:*

   A. Doctor Robert Smith.
   B. Dr. Robert Smith, MD.
   C. Robert Smith, MD.
   D. Dr. Robert Smith.

3. Which refers to *after food*?

   A. a.c.
   B. p.o.
   C. n.p.o.
   D. p.c.

4. Which of these represents the correct expression of *dictated* abbreviations under the DIAGNOSIS heading?

   A. Status post anterior-wall MI.
   B. Urinary tract infection with elevated WBC and positive UA.
   C. Macrocytic anemia; elevation in mean corpuscular volume (MCV) since last blood panel.
   D. Right extremity DVT.

5. An abbreviation that is pronounced as a word is called a/an:

   A. acronym.
   B. initialism.
   C. brief form.
   D. slang form.

6. Which is transcribed correctly?

   A. 82 Elm Avenue, Suite #2
   B. 82 Elm Avenue, Room #1
   C. 82 Elm Avenue, No. 4
   D. 82 Elm Avenue, Apt. No. 4

7. Which represents the preferred expression of an abbreviation?

   A. Walter Evans, Jr.
   B. C. Allen Walker, Ph.D.
   C. WBC's
   D. p.o.'s

8. Use the degree symbol to express:

   A. angles.
   B. temperature.
   C. imaging studies.
   D. All of the above.

9. Which is transcribed correctly?

   A. She presented complaining of nausea and vomiting times 2 days.
   B. She presented complaining of nausea and vomiting x2 days.
   C. She presented complaining of nausea and vomiting x 2 days.
   D. She presented complaining of nausea and vomiting for 2 days.

10. Which of these is *not* on the Joint Commission's "minimum list" of abbreviations required on all *Do Not Use* facility lists?

    A. q.d.
    B. h.s.
    C. IU
    D. q.o.d.

11. On a Joint Commission accreditation survey, which of these is *not* a condition that must be met under open/closed review for a healthcare organization to be considered "in compliance"?

    A. Use of any item on the list is "minimal" (less than 20% of the instances of the intended term are abbreviated or symbolized).
    B. Use of any item on the list is "sporadic" (less than 10% of the instances of the intended term are abbreviated or symbolized).

C. Whenever any prohibited item has been used in any order, there is written evidence of confirmation of the intended meaning before the order is carried out.
D. The organization has implemented a plan for continued improvement to achieve 100 percent compliance.

12. Which is transcribed correctly?

A. She was originally seen by a cardiologist in New Bedford, Mass.
B. We requested films from his orthopedic clinic in Rochester NY.
C. Originally hailing from Little Rock, AR, she married a serviceman and has spent the past 10 years living abroad.
D. He is going to spend the summer in Naples Florida.

13. The Joint Commission requires any organization that did not already have a banned list of abbreviations in place to identify and apply at least another __________ "Do not use" abbreviations, acronyms, and symbols.

A. 3
B. 5
C. 8
D. 10

14. Per AHDI recommendations, when a physician dictates *cc* in a liquid volume expression, the MT in a non-verbatim environment should:

A. leave a blank.
B. transcribe as dictated.
C. flag the report to the attention of the author.
D. change the *cc* to *mL*.

15. Which of these is a correctly abbreviated metric unit of measure?

A. ml
B. MEq
C. dB
D. hz

Proofreading/Editing

Correct the abbreviation errors in each of the sentences below.

1. She was told to take Tylenol prn pain or fever and call the office for fevers over 101.5.
2. The wound measured 3 in and ran laterally outward from just below the xiphoid.
3. TITLE OF OPERATION: ORIF, left radius.
4. She had 2-cm induration with exquisite tenderness behind the left ear lobe.
5. Her CBC's have showed slightly elevated lymph's, which is to be expected.
6. The baby weighed 8 lbs 12 oz.
7. The child is to be given Cortisporin-TC 3 mg AU twice a day.
8. DIAGNOSIS: Pyelonephritis with elevated BUN.
9. ESTIMATED BLOOD LOSS: 200 cc.
10. Xanax .5 mg q.h.s.

Answer Key—Chapter 9

Refer to the answer keys below for answers to practical application exercises for this chapter.

Exam Prep Assessment

1. C
2. B
3. D
4. B
5. A
6. C
7. D
8. D
9. D
10. B

11. A
12. C
13. A
14. D
15. C

Proofreading/Editing

1. She was told to take Tylenol p.r.n. pain or fever and call the office for fevers over 101.5.
2. The wound measured 3 inches and ran laterally outward from just below the xiphoid.
3. TITLE OF OPERATION: Open reduction and internal fixation (ORIF), left radius.
4. She had 2 cm induration with exquisite tenderness behind the left ear lobe.
5. Her CBCs have showed slightly elevated lymphs, which is to be expected.
6. The baby weighed 8 pounds 12 ounces.
7. The child is to be given Cortisporin-TC 3 mg in both ears twice a day.
8. DIAGNOSIS: Pyelonephritis with elevated BUN. *(Correct as dictated).*
9. ESTIMATED BLOOD LOSS: 200 mL.
10. Xanax 0.5 mg at bedtime.

Transcription Practice

Complete the Transcription Practice exercises for Chapter 9 on the CD-ROM included with this text. Answers to these exercises can be found in Appendix A at the back of this book.

CHAPTER 10

Numbers

Learning objectives for this chapter:

- ✓ Understand and apply *Book of Style* (BOS) standards related to numbers and the role of numeric values in the health record.
- ✓ Accurately identify these standards via multiple-choice questions that prepare you for AHDI credentialing examinations.
- ✓ Apply your knowledge of these standards to proofreading/editing exercises that will prepare you for practical application in the workplace and on AHDI credentialing examinations.
- ✓ Apply your knowledge of these standards in a simulated work setting through transcription of sample dictation clips designed to test the standards outlined in this chapter.

Introduction

As you acclimate to transcription and healthcare delivery, you will begin to recognize the critical components of a patient's record. You will begin to identify key inclusions and values upon which further treatment and provision of care rely. This will enable you to apply these, and other standards, consistently in your transcription. Understanding the process of healthcare delivery will be invaluable in applying all of these standards in an informed manner. Human judgment in the documentation process will always be critical to an accurate record. Often, the slightest change in a numeric value, such as the omission or misplacement of a decimal point or comma, can lead to the misinterpretation of core patient data and potentially to the misapplication of that data in a treatment context. While ultimately the provider needs to authenticate that dictation and verify its accuracy, the reality is that in an overburdened healthcare delivery system, providers are not always as careful as they should be, and they rely very heavily on medical transcriptionists to be watchful and vigilant in documenting patient care. Therefore, it is always sound practice to slow down and be extra careful when transcribing these key sections of a patient record, and of course, always flagging a report when that data is unclearly dictated or dictated in error.

Tips and Strategies for this Chapter:

- *Read the chapter thoroughly, highlighting or underlining references that are unfamiliar to you.*
- *Make two index cards or quick reference lists – one that enumerates the instances for using arabic numbers and the other for the instances where roman numerals are required.*
- *Familiarize yourself with the chapter index found in the margin on the first page of this chapter in your BOS (page 227) and practice navigating the chapter using the index.*

Exam Prep Assessment

Apply your understanding and knowledge of Chapter 10 to the multiple-choice exam prep questions below.

1. Which is correct?

   A. D10 and half-normal saline
   B. D5 NS
   C. D5¼ normal saline
   D. D10/0.45 NaCl

2. How should the dictated phrase *"a six two K wire"* be expressed?

   A. 62 K-wire
   B. 6-2 K wire

C. 0.062 K-wire
D. 0.62 K wire

3. Which is transcribed correctly?

   A. Physical examination reveals a 1-year-2-month-old healthy female.
   B. He is 37-years-old and presents with right shoulder pain.
   C. 18-year-old with a compound-complex fracture off the left distal radius.
   D. This 78-year-old Hispanic female was brought to the ER with chest pain.

4. Fill in the blank with the correction expression below.

   Neutrophils _______________.

   A. 68%
   B. .68%
   C. 6.8
   D. 6.8%

5. Which of these requires the use of roman numerals?

   A. diabetes mellitus types
   B. cardiac murmur grades
   C. blood factors
   D. APGAR scores

6. Which is transcribed correctly?

   A. She has been divorced since the late 80s.
   B. She has been divorced since the late 80's.
   C. She has been divorced since the late '80s.
   D. She has been divorced since the late '80's.

7. Choose the correct expression in *military time* for the dictated material below:

   DICTATED: The patient was admitted to the ER at nine thirty this evening.

   A. 0930
   B. 9:30

C. 20:30
D. 2130

8. All of the following are expressed using roman numerals *except*:

    A. cancer grades
    B. cranial nerves
    C. NYHA heart failure classifications
    D. Clark levels

9. What is the roman numeral for 500?

    A. V
    B. D
    C. L
    D. M

10. Which is expressed correctly?

    A. He is the only 1 in his family who has been sick with flu-like symptoms.
    B. The patient complained of zero out of five pain.
    C. She complained that her out-of-pocket expenses were running her in the 1000s of dollars.
    D. He had been given a zero chance of regaining full use of his right hand.

11. All of the following represent the correct transcription of an ordinal number *except:*

    A. I told her we would discuss increasing her activity level somewhere around her fourth or fifth postoperative visit.
    B. She was diagnosed with gestational diabetes in her 6th month of pregnancy.
    C. We last saw him on December 12th, 2007.
    D. There was exquisite tenderness with manipulation of the right fifth metacarpal joint.

12. Use a comma with numeric values:

    A. between words expressing a number.
    B. when only the month and year are given.

C. to separate groups of 3 numerals in numbers of 4 digits or more unless decimals are used.
D. to separate adjacent unrelated numbers if neither can be expressed readily in words.

13. Which is correct?

A. #18-French catheter
B. #18 French catheter
C. 18 French catheter
D. 18 French-catheter

14. What is the equivalent nonmilitary time for *"1730 hours"*?

A. 7:30 a.m.
B. 10:30 a.m.
C. 5:30 p.m.
D. 7:30 p.m.

15. Which is correct?

A. 2-days history
B. 3 months' salary
C. 12 hour medication
D. 6-years' experience

Proofreading/Editing

Correct the punctuation errors in each of the sentences below.

1. This is the patient's eleventh visit to the emergency room this year.

2. White count was eleven thousand with a left shift.

3. She retired in her early 60's.

4. She was admitted and diagnosed with class three cardiac failure.

5. I elicited 0 response to painful stimuli from the patient.

6. 3 days ago she began having pain in the lower back.

7. I last saw him on December 12, 2004 and started him on Prevacid.

8. She handed me 2-dollars worth of quarters in change.

9. A number ten scalpel was used to incise the area.

10. We covered her with a tapering two week course of steroids.

Answer Key – Chapter 10

Refer to the answer keys below for answers to practical application exercises for this chapter.

Exam Prep Assessment

1. D
2. C
3. D
4. A
5. C
6. C
7. D
8. A
9. B
10. D
11. C
12. D
13. A
14. C
15. B

Proofreading/Editing

1. This is the patient's 11th visit to the emergency room this year.
2. White count was 11,000 with a left shift.
3. She retired in her early 60s.

4. She was admitted and diagnosed with class III cardiac failure.
5. I elicited zero response to painful stimuli from the patient.
6. Three days ago she began having pain in the lower back.

   or

   She began having pain in the lower back 3 days ago.
7. I last saw him on December 12, 2004, and started him on Prevacid.
8. She handed me 2 dollars' worth of quarters in change.
9. A #10 scalpel was used to incise the area.
10. We covered her with a tapering 2-week course of steroids.

Transcription Practice

Complete the Transcription Practice exercises for Chapter 10 on the CD-ROM included with this text. Answers to these exercises can be found in Appendix A at the back of this book.

Percents, Proportions, Ratios, and Ranges

Learning objectives for this chapter:

- ✓ Understand and apply *Book of Style* (BOS) standards related to percents/percentages and their use/application in the healthcare record.
- ✓ Understand and apply *Book of Style* (BOS) standards related to proportions and their use/application in the healthcare record.
- ✓ Understand and apply *Book of Style* (BOS) standards related to ratios and their use/application in the healthcare record.
- ✓ Understand and apply *Book of Style* (BOS) standards related to ranges and their use/application in the healthcare record.
- ✓ Accurately identify these standards via multiple-choice questions that prepare you for AHDI credentialing examinations.
- ✓ Apply your knowledge of these standards to proofreading/editing exercises that will prepare you for practical application in the workplace and on AHDI credentialing examinations.
- ✓ Apply your knowledge of these standards in a simulated work setting through transcription of sample dictation clips designed to test the standards outlined in this chapter.

Introduction

The concepts expressed in this chapter relate to value expressions that, when transcribed correctly, will demonstrate your commitment to a high-quality document. Expressing ratios and proportions correctly and understanding and applying the rules related to ranges, while less important where clinical accuracy is concerned, are demonstrable evidence of your understanding of transcription standards. Clinical accuracy, of course, leaves off at the point where all of the health encounter information is recorded accurately. But quality picks up at that point and concerns itself in the way that information is expressed. These are standards of style that speak to the readability of the document and its ability to communicate information in a clear, clean, and concise manner.

Tips and Strategies for this Chapter:

- *Read the chapter thoroughly, highlighting or underlining references that are unfamiliar to you.*
- *Make four index cards or quick-reference lists—listing rules and examples for each section of the chapter (percents, proportions, ratios, and ranges).*
- *Familiarize yourself with the chapter index found in the margin on the first page of this chapter in your BOS (page 261) and practice navigating the chapter using the index.*

Exam Prep Assessment

Apply your understanding and knowledge of Chapter 11 to the multiple-choice exam prep questions below.

1. Which of the following ranges is expressed correctly?

   A. BPs were running low in the 80-90/50-60 range.
   B. Reflexes were 3-4+/5.
   C. WBC was 10-15,000.
   D. She indicated pain at an intensity level of 7 to 8 out of 10.

2. The fractional expression of relationship between one quantity and another whose value is determined by dividing the numerator by the denominator:

   A. range.
   B. ratio.
   C. percent.
   D. radical.

3. Which is transcribed correctly?

   A. Myeloid:erythroid ratio was 5:1.
   B. We injected 0.5% lidocaine with epinephrine 1-100,000.
   C. FEV1:FVC was 50% of predicted.
   D. The ratio of males to females in the study was 2:1.

4. Which represents an accurately expressed range of values?

   A. She admits to smoking 8-10 cigarettes per day.
   B. Repeat scan revealed a 3-4% increase in tumor size compared to the December scan.
   C. She takes between 4-6 Advil every day for chronic headaches.
   D. She was told insurance would only cover 300-1000 dollars for the procedure.

5. Which of these *dictated* proportions would be transcribed with a virgule (/)?

   A. DTRs were 4+ out of 5.
   B. Respirations were 16 per minute.
   C. We will start her on AccuNeb 0.63 milligrams per 3 mL.
   D. She was started on normal saline with 20 milliequivalents of KCL per liter.

6. Choose the correct transcription of the underlined segment below:

   DICTATED: There was significant T wave inversion in precordial leads V one through V four suspicious for pulmonary embolus.

   A. V1-4
   B. V1 through 4
   C. V1-V4
   D. V1 through V4

7. Which is correct?

   A. Differential revealed .60% polys, .15% lymphs, and 0 bands.
   B. Differential revealed 6 percent polys, 15 percent lymphs, and 0 bands.
   C. Differential revealed 60% polys, 15% lymphs, and 0 bands.
   D. Differential revealed 60 percent polys, 15 percent lymphs, and 0 bands.

8. Choose the correct transcription for the underlined segments below:

   DICTATED: She sustained fractures of <u>C five and C six</u> with disk herniation at <u>C four five</u>.

   A. C5-6; C4-5
   B. C5-C6; C4-C5
   C. C5 and C6; C4 and C5
   D. C5 and C6; C4-C5

9. All of the following are conditions for use of a hyphen in a range *except*:

   A. Decimals and/or commas do not appear in the numeric values.
   B. Neither value contains four or more digits.
   C. Neither value is accompanied by a unit of measure.
   D. Neither value is accompanied by a symbol.

10. Choose the correct transcription for the underlined segment below:

    DICTATED: There is a <u>point 3 percent</u> chance statistically for that side effect.

    A. 0.3%
    B. .3 %
    C. 3%
    D. 3.0%

Proofreading/Editing

Correct the errors in each of the sentences below.

1. The patient's blood pressure was in the seventy to eighty over one-twenty range.

2. I told her those side effects occurred in only two to five percent of patients.
3. He was treated with Epinal point five percent drops to both eyes.
4. We instilled epinephrine one to ten thousand into the area of the incision.
5. Ferritin normal value ranges for women are between eighteen and one-sixty nanograms per milliliter.
6. She was given half percent Isopto Carpine drops for her glaucoma.
7. The patient had an FEV to FVC of sixty-five percent.
8. There was some depression in leads V one through V six.
9. VITAL SIGNS: Blood pressure eighty to ninety over one-thirty to one-forty.
10. Fifty percent of his patients are from the inner city.

Answer Key—Chapter 11

Refer to the answer keys below for answers to practical application exercises for this chapter.

Exam Prep Assessment

1. D
2. B
3. D
4. A
5. A
6. D
7. C
8. D
9. C
10. A

Proofreading/Editing

1. The patient's blood pressure was in the 70 to 80 over 120 range.

   or

The patient's blood pressure was in the 70-80 over 120 range.

or

The patient's blood pressure was in the 70/120 to 80/120 range.

2. I told her those side effects occurred in only 2% to 5% of patients.
3. He was treated with Epinal 0.5% drops to both eyes.
4. We instilled epinephrine 1:10,000 into the area of the incision.
5. Ferritin normal value ranges for women are between 18 and 160 ng/mL.
6. She was given 0.5% Isopto Carpine drops for her glaucoma.
7. The patient had an FEV-to-FVC of 65%.
8. There was some depression in leads V1 through V6.
9. VITAL SIGNS: Blood pressure 80-90 over 130-140.

   or

   VITAL SIGNS: Blood pressure 80 to 90 over 130 to 140.
10. Fifty percent of his patients are from the inner city.

Transcription Practice

Complete the Transcription Practice exercises for Chapter 11 on the CD-ROM included with this text. Answers to these exercises can be found in Appendix A at the back of this book.

CHAPTER 12

Units of Measure

Learning objectives for this chapter:

- ✓ Understand and apply *Book of Style* (BOS) standards related to both metric and conventional units of measure.
- ✓ Accurately identify these standards via multiple-choice questions that prepare you for AHDI credentialing examinations.
- ✓ Apply your knowledge of these standards to proofreading/editing exercises that will prepare you for practical application in the workplace and on AHDI credentialing examinations.
- ✓ Apply your knowledge of these standards in a simulated work setting through transcription of sample dictation clips designed to test the standards outlined in this chapter.

Introduction

Taking the time to memorize the many units of measure covered in this chapter will be a wise investment of time as you move into consistent daily transcription. These are terms you will hear frequently, some days in every record you encounter. Some units of measure, like those specific to radiation and nuclear medicine, will be encountered less often or only if you find yourself consistently transcribing in that specialty environment. For the MT who anticipates a career in acute care transcription, however, being familiar with all of these units will be very important.

It may also be helpful when memorizing these units to mentally categorize them by measurement type so that their application in a clinical context will make more sense to you. Knowing that an injectable medication could only be measured in liquid units will predispose you to interpreting those units accurately and *not* using a measurement for length (mm) when a measurement for liquid (mL) is indicated in context.

Tips and Strategies for this Chapter:

- *Read the chapter thoroughly, highlighting or underlining references that are unfamiliar to you.*
- *Make quick reference lists of all units of measure discussed in this chapter, separated into metric and conventional units.*
- *Familiarize yourself with the chapter index found in the margin on the first page of this chapter in your BOS (page 271) and practice navigating the chapter using the index.*

Exam Prep Assessment

Apply your understanding and knowledge of Chapter 12 to the multiple-choice exam prep questions below.

1. Which of the following is *not* a metric unit of measure?

   A. decibel
   B. meter
   C. ampule
   D. gram

2. Which derived unit below is measured in hertz (Hz)?

   A. area
   B. electrical field
   C. force
   D. frequency

3. All of these are correct abbreviations of a metric unit *except*:

   A. kgm
   B. mL
   C. msec
   D. mmHg

4. Which is transcribed correctly?

   A. We made a small, 2-cm incision and threaded the catheter through the opening.
   B. His 7-foot height has contributed to some slight curvature of the upper spine.
   C. There was a jagged 3 inch laceration to the posterior occiput.
   D. Sonogram revealed an ovoid, 2-x-3-cm mass just posterior to the right nipple.

5. Which is the appropriate abbreviation of a nonmetric unit?

   A. yr
   B. sec
   C. mo
   D. hr

6. Normal human temperature on the *Celsius* scale is:

   A. 37°
   B. 63°
   C. 98.6°
   D. 100°

7. Which is correct?

   A. 5′2″
   B. 8 lbs 6 oz
   C. 5 ft 7 in
   D. 6 pounds 4 ounces

8. Mass is measured in:

   A. meters.
   B. kilograms.
   C. moles.
   D. newtons.

9. Which SI unit is considered a dangerous abbreviation?

   A. μg
   B. mcg
   C. mmol
   D. mEq

10. Which of these is an old apothecary unit still used in clinical reference?

    A. pounds
    B. drops
    C. grams
    D. liters

11. All of these are expressed correctly *except*:

    A. 3.2 x 6.8 m^2
    B. 5 sq m
    C. x10,000
    D. 4-x-4 area

12. When expressions of concentration involve *nonmetric* units:

    A. use a virgule (/) and abbreviate the unit.
    B. use a virgule (/) and spell out the unit.
    C. spell out "per" and abbreviate the unit.
    D. spell out "per" and spell out the unit.

13. Which is the correct expression to fill in the blank below?

    The leg was raised to a _______________ angle.

A. 45 degree
B. 45 degrees
C. 45-degree
D. 45-degrees

14. Which unit is used to measure radiation?

A. Hz
B. mCi
C. J
D. Cd

15. Amperes, or amps, are used to measure electrical:

A. current.
B. voltage.
C. resistance.
D. field strength.

Proofreading/Editing

Correct the errors in each of the sentences below.

1. The patient was cooled to 28° C on cardiopulmonary bypass.

2. Defibrillator threshold measurements were 1.1 mA and 600 ohms of resistance with a 16-mV R wave and a 0.6-V threshold.

3. Doppler studies revealed a regurgitant jet across the mitral valve, with a jet velocity of 4.25 m per sec and a gradient of 72 mmHg.

4. A 10-mm trocar was introduced and advanced without difficulty.

5. The proximal portion of the colon was characterized by the presence of multiple nodular areas averaging from 3-to-5-mm in diameter.

6. The dosage is 225 mg per m2 of Taxol and carboplatin.

7. On physical examination, her weight is 203 lbs and height 5 ft, 3.5 in.

8. The patient has already received 2 gm of Rocephin that would provide coverage for the next 24 hours.

9. Cerebral activity over the left side consisted of medium to high amplitude, poorly sustained 5-hertz waveforms.

10. POSTOPERATIVE DIAGNOSIS: Missed abortion at 5.5 weeks.

Answer Key—Chapter 12

Refer to the answer keys below for answers to practical application exercises for this chapter.

Exam Prep Assessment

1. C
2. D
3. A
4. B
5. C
6. A
7. D
8. B
9. A
10. B
11. D
12. D
13. C
14. B
15. A

Proofreading/Editing

1. The patient was cooled to 28 °C on cardiopulmonary bypass.

2. Defibrillator threshold measurements were 1.1 mA and 600 ohms of resistance with a 16 mV R wave and a 0.6 V threshold.

3. Doppler studies revealed a regurgitant jet across the mitral valve, with a jet velocity of 4.25 m/sec and a gradient of 72 mmHg.

4. A 10 mm trocar was introduced and advanced without difficulty.

5. The proximal portion of the colon was characterized by the presence of multiple nodular areas averaging from 3-5 [*or* 3 to 5] mm in diameter.

6. The dosage is 225 mg/m^2 [*or* mg/sq m] of Taxol and carboplatin.

7. On physical examination, her weight is 203 pounds and height 5 feet 3-1/2 inches.

8. The patient has already received 2 g of Rocephin that would provide coverage for the next 24 hours.

9. Cerebral activity over the left side consisted of medium to high amplitude, poorly sustained 5 Hz waveforms.

10. POSTOPERATIVE DIAGNOSIS: Missed abortion at 5-1/2 weeks.

Transcription Practice

Complete the Transcription Practice exercises for Chapter 12 on the CD-ROM included with this text. Answers to these exercises can be found in Appendix A at the back of this book.

CHAPTER 13

Pharmacology

Learning objectives for this chapter:

- ✓ Understand and apply *Book of Style* (BOS) standards related to chemical nomenclature and drug nomenclatures.
- ✓ Understand and apply *Book of Style* (BOS) standards related to pharmacology.
- ✓ Accurately identify these standards via multiple-choice questions that prepare you for AHDI credentialing examinations.
- ✓ Apply your knowledge of these standards to proofreading/editing exercises that will prepare you for practical application in the workplace and on AHDI credentialing examinations.
- ✓ Apply your knowledge of these standards in a simulated work setting through transcription of sample dictation clips designed to test the standards outlined in this chapter.

Introduction

As a student or new practitioner in medical transcription, you will likely study pharmacology as a separate course component and become familiar with the types, classifications, descriptions, and applications of core drug groups, particularly as they relate to the clinical specialties you study in your terminology, anatomy, and disease sections of study. In addition, you will be expected to recognize many commonly prescribed drugs by specialty and use. This chapter explores the standards of style related to the transcription of drug terminology and chemical nomenclature. Both entail some very specific rules for *how* this information should be represented in writing, and as always, the focus is on clarity of communication in the record.

Some of the chemical references covered in this chapter are rather obscure and rarely encountered. Certainly you will not likely be asked to transcribe chemical formulas in mainstream patient care documentation. You may, however, find yourself employed or contracted by a physician or practice that is involved in research, clinical trials, and case studies, the documentation of which is critical for publication. It is not uncommon for an MT to transcribe this ancillary kind of documentation in those settings. You may, then, encounter more detailed scientific data and references to chemical formulas and processes that you would not typically find in patient records. In the instance of research being documented for formal publication in a medical journal, understanding the appropriate style for transcribing that data will be very valuable to the MT in that setting and an asset to the physician(s) in that practice.

Tips and Strategies for this Chapter:

- *Read the chapter thoroughly, highlighting or underlining references that are unfamiliar to you.*
- *Make index cards or quick-reference lists of the drugs of abuse schedule, providing the most common examples that fall into each schedule.*
- *Make an index card or quick-reference list of Latin dosage abbreviations, which you will encounter/use frequently in the workplace.*
- *Familiarize yourself with the chapter index found in the margin on the first page of this chapter in your BOS (page 293) and practice navigating the chapter using the index.*

Exam Prep Assessment

Apply your understanding and knowledge of Chapter 13 to the multiple-choice exam prep questions below.

1. Which of these is the *chemical name* for a commonly prescribed medication?

   A. aspirin
   B. acetylsalicylic acid

C. Bayer
D. acetaminophen

2. Schedule III drugs are those deemed to have:

   A. high risk for abuse/dependence for which there is no current recognized clinical application/use.
   B. some risk for abuse/dependence but also have a high degree of clinical application/use.
   C. low risk for abuse/dependence and are used for clinical research or represent use of other schedule drugs in limited amounts.
   D. high risk for abuse/dependence that also have some clinical application/use.

3. Which of these is an acceptable expression of a dosage?

   A. Accutane 0.25 mg/kg BID
   B. Lodine 200 mg every 4-6h
   C. Zocor 20 mg b.i.d. q.h.s.
   D. Cefotaxime 50 mg/kg per dose q.12 h. IV

4. A medication that is prescribed to be taken *p.c.* should be taken:

   A. before food.
   B. by mouth.
   C. at bedtime.
   D. after food.

5. Which of these is a schedule II drug?

   A. heroin
   B. codeine
   C. phenobarbital
   D. methadone

6. Atoms of the same element that have different atomic masses are called:

   A. isotopes.
   B. ions.

C. anions.
D. prions.

7. What is the drug name equivalent for vitamin C?

A. riboflavin
B. ascorbic acid
C. thiamine hydrochloride
D. ergocalciferol

8. All of these are correctly expressed herbs or supplements *except*:

A. ginger.
B. Mugwort.
C. ginseng.
D. Hypericum perforatum.

9. Granulocyte colony-stimulating factors (G-CSFs) can be identified by the suffix:

A. –plestim.
B. –mostim.
C. –gramostim.
D. –grastim.

10. Which of these have antineoplastic, antiviral, and/or immuno-modulating properties?

A. hormones
B. interferons
C. interleukins
D. cytokines

11. The chemical symbol *Fe* refers to which element on the periodic table?

A. gold
B. silver
C. iron
D. aluminum

12. How many phases of clinical study or trial does a new drug typically go through prior to FDA approval?

    A. 1
    B. 2
    C. 3
    D. 5

13. Which of these is also known as the *proprietary* name of a drug?

    A. brand
    B. trade
    C. generic
    D. code

14. The appropriate abbreviation for *subcutaneous* is:

    A. subQ
    B. subq
    C. sub cu
    D. subcu

15. All of these are pharmaceutical measurements retained from the avoirdupois system *except*:

    A. grain
    B. ounce
    C. dram
    D. pound

Proofreading/Editing

Correct the punctuation errors in each of the sentences below.

1. He was sent home on erythromycin 500 mg Q.I.D., Theo-Dur 300 mg B.I.D., and Tenormin 50 mg Q.D.

2. She is given 12 Thorazine 25 mg suppositories to use 1 or 2 q.6 hours prn.

3. Serum vitamin-B12 level was 598, well within normal limits.

4. On her last visit she was begun on Nifedipine 20 mg PO and I will increase this to 30 mg.

5. We first injected 5.17 MCI of TC-99M intravenously.

6. The patient will be given Actimmune, an interferon gamma 1-B, for her CGD.

7. Laboratory tests indicated significant anemia, so we have given her 10,000 units of Epoetin alpha.

8. She was given KCL 15 mEq q.i.d.

9. Initial electrolytes revealed Sodium 130, Potassium 4, Chloride 99, and Bicarbonate 12.

10. He will follow up with me q.weekly until this resolves.

Answer Key—Chapter 13

Refer to the answer keys below for answers to practical application exercises for this chapter.

Exam Prep Assessment

1. B
2. B
3. D
4. D
5. D
6. A
7. B
8. B
9. D
10. B
11. C
12. C
13. A
14. D
15. C

Proofreading/Editing

1. He was sent home on erythromycin 500 mg q.i.d., Theo-Dur 300 mg b.i.d., and Tenormin 50 mg daily.

2. She is given 12 Thorazine 25 mg suppositories to use 1 or 2 q.6 h. p.r.n.

3. Serum vitamin B12 [*or* B_{12}] level was 598, well within normal limits.

4. On her last visit she was begun on nifedipine 20 mg p.o., and I will increase this to 30 mg.

5. We first injected 5.17 mCi of Tc 99m [*or* ^{99m}Tc] intravenously.

6. The patient will be given Actimmune, an interferon gamma-1b, for her CGD.

7. Laboratory tests indicated significant anemia, so we have given her 10,000 units of epoetin alfa.

8. She was given KCl 15 mEq q.i.d.

9. Initial electrolytes revealed sodium 130, potassium 4, chloride 99 and bicarbonate 12.

10. He will follow up with me weekly [*or* every week] until this resolves.

Transcription Practice

Complete the Transcription Practice exercises for Chapter 13 on the CD-ROM included with this text. Answers to these exercises can be found in Appendix A at the back of this book.

CHAPTER 14

Cardiology

Learning objectives for this chapter:

- ✓ Understand and apply *Book of Style* (BOS) standards related to the anatomy, physiology, and pathology in cardiology.
- ✓ Understand and apply *Book of Style* (BOS) standards related to diagnostic testing and procedures in cardiology.
- ✓ Understand and apply *Book of Style* (BOS) standards related to cardiovascular classification systems.
- ✓ Accurately identify these standards via multiple-choice questions that prepare you for AHDI credentialing examinations.
- ✓ Apply your knowledge of these standards to proofreading/editing exercises that will prepare you for practical application in the workplace and on AHDI credentialing examinations.
- ✓ Apply your knowledge of these standards in a simulated work setting through transcription of sample dictation clips designed to test the standards outlined in this chapter.

Introduction

Cardiopulmonary medicine represents a core specialty in acute care. Patients present to and are admitted to the hospital for a wide variety of complex conditions, including hypertension, stroke, heart failure, cardiac arrhythmias, valvular heart disease, congenital heart disease, and pulmonary thromboembolisms, the management of which involves a wide array of highly specialized radiologic and diagnostic procedures. Electrocardiography, vector cardiography, electrophysiologic studies, ultrasound, nuclear cardiology, radiology, catheterization, and pulmonary function testing are among these complex studies that an MT will encounter when transcribing in either the acute care setting or in private practice. Since these conditions are common and so often chronic, the MT will encounter references to them and their related studies in almost every medical specialty.

This chapter is designed to orient you to the standards of style specific to the specialty of cardiology. Ideally, this section should be studied in conjunction with learning the anatomy, physiology, disease processes, etc., related to both of these complex specialties. Attempting to work through this chapter without a fundamental understanding of the body systems, conditions, symptoms, tests and procedures related to these specialties could prove confusing and difficult. This chapter should also be coordinated with transcription application in these specialties so that the standards covered here can be reinforced through hands-on practice.

Tips and Strategies for this Chapter:

- *Read the chapter thoroughly, highlighting or underlining references that are unfamiliar to you.*
- *Make index cards or quick-reference lists for the classification systems outlined in this chapter.*
- *Make index cards or quick-reference lists for heart sounds, murmurs, electrocardiogram leads, tracing terms, etc.*
- *Familiarize yourself with the chapter index found in the margin on the first page of this chapter in your BOS (page 317) and practice navigating the chapter using the index.*

Exam Prep Assessment

Apply your understanding and knowledge of Chapter 14 to the multiple-choice exam prep questions below.

1. EKG bipolar leads should be expressed with:

   A. arabic numbers.
   B. lowercase *a*, capital *V*, and *R*, *L* or *F*.
   C. capital *V* followed by an arabic number.
   D. roman numerals.

2. The Braunwauld system is used to classify:

   A. myocardial infarction.
   B. heart failure.
   C. unstable angina.
   D. atrial fibrillation.

3. Which of these terms is not used by the AHA to classify atrial fibrillation?

   A. pervasive
   B. paroxysmal
   C. persistent
   D. permanent

4. A physician who orders a *TEE* is ordering an ________________ of the heart.

   A. electrocardiogram
   B. electroencephalogram
   C. electromyogram
   D. echocardiogram

5. Which of these is expressed correctly?

   A. normal STT wave
   B. normal ST and T-wave
   C. normal ST-T-wave
   D. normal ST and T wave

6. How many heart sounds are assessed on auscultation?

   A. 1
   B. 2

C. 3
D. 4

7. All of these are components assessed on auscultation of the heart *except*:

A. A2
B. M1
C. P2
D. C1

8. Diastolic murmurs are graded on a scale of:

A. 1 to 4.
B. 1 to 6.
C. 1 to 3.
D. 1 to 5.

9. A systolic murmur that is so loud it can be heard with the stethoscope just above the chest wall would be classified as:

A. grade 1.
B. grade 2.
C. grade 3.
D. grade 6.

10. Which of these murmurs is expressed correctly?

A. grade 3-1/2 to 4 over 6
B. grade 3.5/6 to 4/6
C. grade 3.5-4 over 6
D. grade 3.5-4/6

11. In the pacemaker reference *DDDR*, the second *D* refers to which measurement?

A. chambers paced
B. rate modulation
C. chambers sensed
D. response to sensing

12. Which of these systems is used to classify cardiac function after MI?

   A. NYHA
   B. CCS
   C. Braunwald
   D. Forrester

13. Which is correct?

   Coronary angiography revealed ________________ flow.

   A. TIMI 3
   B. TIMI3
   C. TIMI III
   D. TIMI three

14. Class I heart failure represents a patient in whom the degree of failure is:

   A. absent.
   B. asymptomatic.
   C. symptomatic with normal activity.
   D. symptomatic at rest.

15. Which is correct?

   ______________ revealed no evidence of septal or valvular defect.

   A. Three-D echo
   B. 3-D echo
   C. 3D echo
   D. 3D echocardiogram

Proofreading/Editing

Correct the errors in each of the sentences below.

1. She had ST segment depression in leads 2, 3, and AVL.

2. Examination revealed a positive grade II/VI systolic murmur.

3. The patient had T wave inversions in V-4 through V-6.
4. He has been following her for her class-2 cardiac failure.
5. Heart sounds are regular, with S-1 and S-2 normal.
6. There is a faint 1-1/2 over 6 systolic ejection murmur.
7. There is a diphasic T-wave in 2, 3, AVF, V5 and 6.
8. DIAGNOSIS: Status post implantation of AICD.
9. The ST segments are depressed in leads V1-6.
10. Arterial blood gases revealed Po2 and PCo2 to be within normal limits.

Answer Key—Chapter 14

Refer to the answer keys below for answers to practical application exercises for this chapter.

Exam Prep Assessment

1. D
2. C
3. A
4. D
5. B
6. D
7. D
8. A
9. D
10. B
11. C
12. D
13. B
14. B
15. D

Proofreading/Editing

1. She had ST segment depression in leads II, III, and aVL.
2. Examination revealed a positive grade 2/6 systolic murmur.
3. The patient had T-wave inversions in V4 through V6.
4. He has been following her for her class II cardiac failure.
5. Heart sounds are regular, with S1 and S2 normal.
6. There is a faint 1.5 over 6 systolic ejection murmur.

   or

   There is a faint 1.5/6 systolic ejection murmur.
7. There is a diphasic T wave in II, III, aVF, V5 and V6.
8. DIAGNOSIS: Status post implantation of automatic implantable cardioverter-defibrillator.
9. The ST segments are depressed in leads V1 through V6.
10. Arterial blood gases revealed PO2 and PCO2 to be within normal limits.

Transcription Practice

Complete the Transcription Practice exercises for Chapter 14 on the CD-ROM included with this text. Answers to these exercises can be found in Appendix A at the back of this book.

[illegible]

CHAPTER 15

Genetics

Learning objectives for this chapter:

- ✓ Understand and apply *Book of Style* (BOS) standards related to human gene nomenclature and chromosome expression.
- ✓ Understand and apply *Book of Style* (BOS) standards related to nonhuman gene nomenclature.
- ✓ Accurately identify these standards via multiple-choice questions that prepare you for AHDI credentialing examinations.
- ✓ Apply your knowledge of these standards to proofreading/editing exercises that will prepare you for practical application in the workplace and on AHDI credentialing examinations.
- ✓ Apply your knowledge of these standards in a simulated work setting through transcription of sample dictation clips designed to test the standards outlined in this chapter.

Introduction

The headway made by scientists in unraveling the human genome will have a tremendous impact on the future of medicine and health care. If you are a student or new MT, you are entering the profession at the dawning age of genomics and should expect to hear more references to these terms as they correlate to the diagnosis and treatment of disease. The detection and treatment of a particular cancer, genetic defect, or neuromuscular disease will not likely be the same 10 years from now as it is today, and much of that will be attributable to breakthroughs in genomic research.

Genetic testing can be performed to establish the identity of an individual or the relationship between individuals as in forensic medicine or paternity testing. It can be used to detect hereditary disorders in newborns, both prior to and after birth. The application of genetic testing to the specialty of oncology, for example, is increasingly more prevalent. Screening for oncogenes that indicate a predetermined risk for certain cancers is now a standard practice for many oncologists.

The information provided in this chapter related to genetics is very complex and encountered infrequently in mainstream dictation. However, you will likely continue to hear more references to genetics and genomic research through your career. Probably more than any generation of medical transcriptionists who came before you, you will represent the generation of MTs whose work will be greatly impacted by research in the genomic discipline.

Tips and Strategies for this Chapter:

- *Read the chapter thoroughly, highlighting or underlining references that are unfamiliar to you.*
- *Familiarize yourself with the chapter index found in the margin on the first page of this chapter in your BOS (page 333) and practice navigating the chapter using the index.*

Exam Prep Assessment

Apply your understanding and knowledge of Chapter 15 to the multiple-choice exam prep questions below.

1. HIV and other retroviruses contain __________ main *structural* genes.

   A. 2
   B. 3
   C. 5
   D. 10

2. The chromosome complement of an individual, tissue, or cell is called a/an:

   A. arm.
   B. serotype.
   C. karyotype.
   D. band.

3. All of the following are true of oncogenes *except*:

   A. they typically play a role in healthy growth unless mutated.
   B. they were first identified in bacteria.
   C. they are expressed in formal publication in italics.
   D. they are expressed in transcription in three-letter lowercase regular type.

4. Which word is used to describe tumor genes that normally restrict cellular growth but when missing or inactivated, they allow cells to grow at an uncontrolled rate.

   A. helper
   B. inducer
   C. reducer
   D. suppressor

5. Deoxyribonucleic acid contains all of the following bases *except:*

   A. uracil.
   B. cytosine.
   C. adenine.
   D. guanine.

6. How would *heterogenous ribonucleic acid* be expressed in abbreviated form?

   A. heterogenous RNA
   B. HRNA
   C. hnRNA
   D. hRNA

7. Mutations of the *BRCA-1* gene are associated with cancer of the:

   A. brain.

B. bladder.
C. breast.
D. bone.

8. In the gene reference *TNF*, the *N* refers to:

A. name.
B. necrosis.
C. number.
D. nucleic.

9. Which is expressed correctly?

A. We will test for the cystic fibrosis transmembrane conductance regulator gene (CFTR).
B. The role for TGF-β-1 gene application in pulmonary disease was discussed with the patient.
C. The RRNA-based test detected ocular *C trachomatis* infection in 60% of our case subjects.
D. She has 21-hydroxylase deficiency, which I explained to her is a mutation of the 6P-21.3 chromosome.

10. Which represents the correct transcription of a genetic reference?

A. alfa-fetoprotein
B. beta II microglobulin
C. alpha-fetoprotein
D. beta 2 microglobulin

Proofreading/Editing

Correct the errors in each of the sentences below.

1. DIAGNOSIS: Klinefelter's syndrome (47-XXY).

2. Because of the clinical suspicion of mosaic Turner syndrome, a chromosome analysis is recommended to clarify whether the 45 X cells represent true mosaicism.

3. Of note, tumor suppressor gene CDKN-1a has been shown to be involved both in stress response mechanisms and in the expression of genes implicated in age-related diseases.

4. She had previously been worked up for the Huntington disease (HD) gene, which came back negative.

5. The APOE e2 allele has been shown to greatly increase the risk of a rare condition called hyperlipoproteinemia type III.

6. An SS-DNA to DS-DNA ratio of less than 1.0 indicates the absence of SS-DNA antibodies.

Answer Key – Chapter 15

Refer to the answer keys below for answers to practical application exercises for this chapter.

Exam Prep Assessment

1. B
2. C
3. B
4. D
5. A
6. C
7. C
8. B
9. A
10. C

Proofreading/Editing

1. DIAGNOSIS: Klinefelter syndrome (47,XXY).

2. Because of the clinical suspicion of mosaic Turner syndrome, a chromosome analysis is recommended to clarify whether the 45,X cells represent true mosaicism.

3. Of note, tumor suppressor gene CDKN1A has been shown to be involved both in stress response mechanisms and in the expression of genes implicated in age-related diseases.

4. She had previously been worked up for the Huntington disease gene, HD, which came back negative.

5. The APOE*E2 allele has been shown to greatly increase the risk of a rare condition called hyperlipoproteinemia type III.

6. An ssDNA-to-dsDNA ratio of less than 1.0 indicates the absence of ssDNA antibodies.

Transcription Practice

Complete the Transcription Practice exercises for Chapter 15 on the CD-ROM included with this text. Answers to these exercises can be found in Appendix A at the back of this book.

CHAPTER 16

Hematology Oncology

Learning objectives for this chapter:

- ✓ Understand and apply *Book of Style* (BOS) standards related to blood and hematology.
- ✓ Understand and apply *Book of Style* (BOS) standards related to oncology.
- ✓ Accurately identify these standards via multiple-choice questions that prepare you for AHDI credentialing examinations.
- ✓ Apply your knowledge of these standards to proofreading/editing exercises that will prepare you for practical application in the workplace and on AHDI credentialing examinations.
- ✓ Apply your knowledge of these standards in a simulated work setting through transcription of sample dictation clips designed to test the standards outlined in this chapter.

Introduction

Examinations performed on body fluids, such as blood, cerebrospinal fluid, waste products, and abnormal products (calculi, for example) are critical to the diagnosis and treatment of disease. These types of examinations fall under a branch of pathology called clinical pathology that is focused on quantitative analysis in these areas. Anatomic pathology, on the other hand, deals with the gross and microscopic evaluation of living human tissue to determine the presence, extent, and evolution of disease. Both branches are encountered constantly in healthcare documentation, both in the documentation of laboratory tests and values and the pathologic findings reported in multiple specialties, most specifically *oncology*.

Recognizing and applying standards that relate to laboratory medicine will require an in-depth understanding of blood and tissue anatomy, basic hematology and histology, and the disease process of malignancy. The *Book of Style* provides standards specific to the transcription of blood references, laboratory tests and values, and cancer medicine. Given the high degree of potential error associated with this area of a patient's report, transcriptionists are encouraged to be particularly vigilant in both preparation and application of these standards. The incorrect transcription or transposition of a lab name or value or an error in transcribing the classification of disease in an oncology report could carry potential for risk to the patient. This represents an area of the report where clarity and accuracy are crucial, and transcriptionists need to be extra cautious here.

Tips and Strategies for this Chapter:

- *Read the chapter thoroughly, highlighting or underlining references that are unfamiliar to you.*
- *Make index cards or quick reference lists for the blood types, blood cell types, and blood factors for future use, as these will be encountered virtually daily throughout your career.*
- *Make index cards or quick reference lists for the grading and staging systems used in oncology, including meaning and appropriate expression.*
- *Familiarize yourself with the chapter index found in the margin on the first page of this chapter in your BOS (page 343) and practice navigating the chapter using the index.*

Exam Prep Assessment

Apply your understanding and knowledge of Chapter 16 to the multiple-choice exam prep questions below.

1. A reference to *MX* in the TNM staging system for malignant tumors means:

   A. there is no evidence of primary tumor.
   B. there is no regional lymph node metastasis.

C. the extent of the metastasis cannot be determined.
D. carcinoma in situ.

2. In a healthy human body, eosinophils account for ________ of the formed elements in the blood.

A. 65%
B. 25%
C. 6%
D. 4%

3. Which is expressed correctly?

A. LABORATORIES: WBC 4200, H/H 12.6 and 34.
B. LABORATORIES: WBC 4200, H&H 12.6 and 34.
C. LABORATORIES: WBC 4200, hemoglobin 12.6, and hematocrit 34.
D. LABORATORIES: WBC 4200, hemoglobin and hematocrit 12.6 and 34.

4. Which represents an accurately transcribed blood type?

A. Her blood type is A+.
B. According to the chart, he is B negative and we've ordered type and crossmatch.
C. EBL was 2000 cc, and we transfused 2 units of O-negative.
D. He was given rapid transfusion of B- blood in the ER.

5. Blood factor IX is also known as the ______________ factor.

A. Stuart
B. Hageman
C. Christmas
D. antihemophilic

6. All of these are tests performed under flow cytometry *except:*

A. histocompatibility panel.
B. acute leukemia panel.
C. lymphoma panel.
D. LGL panel.

7. Which is expressed correctly?

   A. DIAGNOSIS: T2, N1, M1 adenocarcinoma of the right breast.
   B. DIAGNOSIS: T2-N1-M1 adenocarcinoma of the right breast.
   C. DIAGNOSIS: T2 N1 M1 adenocarcinoma of the right breast.
   D. DIAGNOSIS: T2N1M1 adenocarcinoma of the right breast.

8. Which of these is a staging system for colon cancer?

   A. Broders index
   B. Astler-Coller
   C. Dukes
   D. Gleason

9. Radiation therapy is measured in:

   A. Hertz.
   B. joules.
   C. centigray.
   D. waveforms.

10. The Jewett system is used to classify carcinoma of the:

   A. breast.
   B. bladder.
   C. brain.
   D. prostate.

11. Nonlymphoid leukemia that is classified as M5 is defined as:

   A. myeloblastic.
   B. promyelocytic.
   C. monocytic.
   D. erythroleukemia.

12. Which is expressed correctly?

   A. Myeloid-to-erythroid ratio
   B. Myeloid/erythroid ratio

C. Myeloid:erythroid ratio
D. M:E ratio

13. What blood factor is deficient in von Willebrand disease?

A. Factor X
B. Factor IV
C. Factor XII
D. Factor VIII

14. All of these are clotting factor variants *except:*

A. Factor V Leiden.
B. Prower factor.
C. factor V Cambridge.
D. fibrinogen Paris.

15. Which of these is *not* a term used to describe red cell morphology?

A. Howell-Jolly bodies
B. Stippling
C. Monophilic
D. Rouleaux

Proofreading/Editing

Correct the errors in each of the sentences below.

1. LABORATORY DATA: White count 33 hundred with H&H of 19 and 34.5.

2. She presents today to initiate mop treatment for her Hodgkin's lymphoma.

3. She was found to have PT-1 PN-0 PM-X neuroblastoma.

4. The patient has Clark level 3 malignant melanoma.

5. Bone marrow aspirate examination was performed on 2 right slides.

6. PROCEDURE: XBRT with consecutive fractions of 3 centigray per session over 6 treatments.

7. DIAGNOSIS: FIGO stage 2b ovarian carcinoma.

8. She did have a Pap last year that revealed CIN I neoplasia, but repeat Pap was normal.

9. He has Factor 5 Leiden thrombophilia, diagnosed in his early 30's.

10. We will be tracking the patient's helper-inducer T-cells closely.

Answer Key—Chapter 16

Refer to the answer keys below for answers to practical application exercises for this chapter.

Exam Prep Assessment

1. C
2. D
3. C
4. B
5. C
6. A
7. D
8. B
9. C
10. B
11. C
12. A
13. D
14. B
15. C

Proofreading/Editing

1. LABORATORY DATA: White count 3300 with hemoglobin 19 and hematocrit 34.5.

2. She presents today to initiate MOPP treatment for her Hodgkin lymphoma.

3. She was found to have pT1pN0pMX neuroblastoma.

4. The patient has Clark level III malignant melanoma.

5. Bone marrow aspirate examination was performed on 2 Wright slides.

6. PROCEDURE: External beam radiation therapy (XBRT) with consecutive fractions of 3 cGy per session over 6 treatments.

7. DIAGNOSIS: FIGO stage IIb ovarian carcinoma.

8. She did have a Pap last year that revealed CIN-I neoplasia, but repeat Pap was normal.

9. He has factor V Leiden thrombophilia, diagnosed in his early 30s.

10. We will be tracking the patient's helper/inducer T cells closely.

Transcription Practice

Complete the Transcription Practice exercises for Chapter 16 on the CD-ROM included with this text. Answers to these exercises can be found in Appendix A at the back of this book.

Dermatology Allergy Immunology

Learning objectives for this chapter:

- ✓ Understand and apply *Book of Style* (BOS) standards related to dermatology and allergic medicine.
- ✓ Understand and apply *Book of Style* (BOS) standards related to immunology.
- ✓ Accurately identify these standards via multiple-choice questions that prepare you for AHDI credentialing examinations.
- ✓ Apply your knowledge of these standards to proofreading/editing exercises that will prepare you for practical application in the workplace and on AHDI credentialing examinations.
- ✓ Apply your knowledge of these standards in a simulated work setting through transcription of sample dictation clips designed to test the standards outlined in this chapter.

Introduction

Clinical dermatology is dedicated to the identification, diagnosis, and treatment of skin diseases that are associated with both external and internal diseases and also to potentially disabling or fatal skin diseases that often require systemic drug therapy. This can range from carcinomas to autoimmune blistering disorders (pemphigus, pemphigoid), cutaneous T-cell lymphoma to widespread psoriasis, and severe drug reactions (Stevens-Johnson Syndrome, toxic epidermal necrolysis) to skin diseases associated with connective tissue disorders (lupus erythematosus, dermatomyositis, scleroderma, and vasculitis).

Allergies are an abnormal response of the immune system. People who have allergies have an immune system that reacts to a usually harmless substance in the environment. This substance (pollen, mold, animal dander, etc.) is called an allergen. Clinical immunology refers to the spectrum of diseases that are also abnormal responses of the immune system; including deficiencies that cause reduced ability to combat infections and over-activities of the immune system that cause reactions to drugs and insect stings.

Tips and Strategies for this Chapter:

- *Read the chapter thoroughly, highlighting or underlining references that are unfamiliar to you.*
- *Make index cards or quick-reference lists for the foreign terms and classification systems outlined in this chapter.*
- *Make quick-reference lists for immunologic terms and nomenclatures outlined in this chapter.*
- *Familiarize yourself with the chapter index found in the margin on the first page of this chapter in your BOS (page 365) and practice navigating the chapter using the index.*

Exam Prep Assessment

Apply your understanding and knowledge of Chapter 17 to the multiple-choice exam prep questions below.

1. All of these are types of lymphocytes *except*:

   A. stem cells.
   B. T cells.
   C. B cells.
   D. natural killer cells.

2. Which of these proteins induces growth and differentiation of lymphocytes and hematopoietic stem cells?

   A. immunoglobulins
   B. interferons

C. interleukins
D. colony-stimulating factors

3. Which of these is correctly expressed?

A. scarlatiniforme
B. herpetiform
C. glioblastoma multiform
D. zosteriforme

4. All of these are tests for allergies *except:*

A. RAST.
B. Mohs technique.
C. patch testing.
D. challenge testing.

5. In the *ABCDE* system for describing the detection of melanoma, *B* refers to an irregularity in:

A. blood.
B. basal cells.
C. borders.
D. body position.

6. Which represents the correct transcription of the missing information in the excerpt below?

The patient was admitted to the emergency room with ____________________ of both palms.

A. second degree burns
B. second-degree burns
C. 2nd degree burns
D. 2nd-degree burns

7. An adult with burns to the entire right arm and right leg would have burns to what percentage of total body under the rule of nines?

   A. 9%
   B. 18%
   C. 27%
   D. 36%

8. Which Clark level represents invasion of primary malignant melanoma into the subcutaneous fat?

   A. level I
   B. level II
   C. level III
   D. level IV

9. *CX3C* is an example of a/an:

   A. cytokine.
   B. human leukocyte antigen.
   C. immunoglobulin.
   D. interleukin.

10. Which of these is subdivided into compounds that are referenced by Greek letters such as *alfa, beta,* and *gamma*?

    A. lymphocytes
    B. interferons
    C. immunoglobulins
    D. chemokines

11. Which of these is correct?

    A. Nursing notes revealed worsening of the grade 2 decubiti of the patient's gluteal folds.
    B. Nursing notes revealed worsening of the grade 2 decubitus ulcers of the patient's gluteal folds.

C. Nursing notes revealed worsening of the stage II decubiti of the patient's gluteal folds.
D. Nursing notes reveal worsening of the stage II decubitus ulcers of the patient's gluteal folds.

12. The Breslow classification system measures tumor:

A. diameter.
B. color.
C. thickness.
D. malignancy.

13. The least abundant immunoglobulin in human serum is:

A. IgG.
B. IgA.
C. IgD.
D. IgE.

14. The suffix –*leukin* identifies which interleukin derivative?

A. 1a
B. 2
C. 4
D. 6

15. Which is expressed correctly?

A. The patient had a helper:suppressor ration of 0.7.
B. The patient had a helper/suppressor ratio of 0.7.
C. The patient had a helper-suppressor ratio of 0.7.
D. The patient had a helper suppressor ratio of 0.7.

Proofreading/Editing

Correct the errors in each of the sentences below.

1. The patient had transient CD4-plus T lymphocytopenia that later resolved.

2. We discussed the polyneuropathy that can be associated with IGG and IGA monoclonal gammopathy.

3. Given the full thickness burns she has sustained to the posterior trunk and left leg, we have calculated her impairment at 18% under the rule of 9's.

4. DIAGNOSIS: Malignant melanoma, Clark's level 3.

5. Oral exam revealed significant herpetiforme aphthous lesions, clustered and of 1 to 2 mm in size.

6. I explained the risks and benefits of Moh's versus excisional biopsy, and the patient has opted for Moh's surgery.

7. Given the fact that HLAB-27 has been associated with ankylosing spondylitis, we will have this drawn and sent off for analysis.

8. Recent literature seems to suggest that a small subset of human T cells expresses low levels of pan-B-lymphs.

9. Despite frequent irrigation and debridement, her stage 4 decubital ulcers have not improved.

10. Examination of the skin reveals multiple cafe aulait spots on the chest and arms.

Answer Key—Chapter 17

Refer to the answer keys below for answers to practical application exercises for this chapter.

Exam Prep Assessment

1. A
2. C
3. B
4. B
5. C
6. C
7. C
8. D
9. A
10. B

11. D
12. C
13. D
14. B
15. C

Proofreading/Editing

1. The patient had transient CD4+ T-lymphocytopenia that later resolved.
2. We discussed the polyneuropathy that can be associated with IgG and IgA monoclonal gammopathy.
3. Given the full-thickness burns she has sustained to the entire posterior trunk and approximately half of the left leg, we have calculated her extent as 27% under the rule of nines.

Note: In a verbatim environment or one where editing this value would fall outside of editing guidelines, the MT should leave a blank and flag the report, asking the physician to verify the calculation based on the reference to entire trunk (18% under the rule of nines) and half the leg (9% under the rule of nines).

4. DIAGNOSIS: Malignant melanoma, Clark level III.
5. Oral exam revealed significant herpetiform aphthous lesions, clustered and of 1 to 2 mm in size.
6. I explained the risks and benefits of Mohs versus excisional biopsy, and the patient has opted for Mohs surgery.
7. Given the fact that HLA-B27 has been associated with ankylosing spondylitis, we will have this drawn and sent off for analysis.
8. Recent literature seems to suggest that a small subset of human T cells expresses low levels of pan-B lymphocytes.
9. Despite frequent irrigation and debridement, her stage IV decubitus ulcers have not improved.
10. Examination of the skin reveals multiple café au lait spots on the chest and arms.

Transcription Practice

Complete the Transcription Practice exercises for Chapter 17 on the CD-ROM included with this text. Answers to these exercises can be found in Appendix A at the back of this book.

CHAPTER 18

Orthopedics Neurology

Learning objectives for this chapter:

- ✓ Understand and apply *Book of Style* (BOS) standards related to orthopedics.
- ✓ Understand and apply *Book of Style* (BOS) standards related to neurology.
- ✓ Accurately identify these standards via multiple-choice questions that prepare you for AHDI credentialing examinations.
- ✓ Apply your knowledge of these standards to proofreading/editing exercises that will prepare you for practical application in the workplace and on AHDI credentialing examinations.
- ✓ Apply your knowledge of these standards in a simulated work setting through transcription of sample dictation clips designed to test the standards outlined in this chapter.

Introduction

This chapter will orient you to the standards of style specific to complex but fascinating specialties of orthopedics and neurology—two closely related specialties that often have intersecting diagnostic implications. Depending on the format of your transcription program, this chapter can provide an excellent opportunity for introduction to surgical transcription. Orthopedic surgery offers a broad-based orientation to materials, equipment, and positional/directional terms that will be encountered across multiple specialties. In addition, it provides a wealth of procedural terms that are complex and unique to the specialty.

Transcribing operative reports can often feel like you are right there in the procedure room with the physician. In fact, in the early days of patient care documentation, medical secretaries often sat in a corner of the operating room, taking shorthand notes from the physician, who dictated throughout the procedure. Those notes were later transcribed on a manual typewriter for inclusion in the patient's record. While those days are long behind us, operative reports are still a critical part of the care record, and most MTs find them to be among the most interesting reports they are tasked with transcribing. New MTs, however, can find complex procedures to be challenging and frustrating. In specialties like Orthopedics and Neurology, the anatomical terms, surgical equipment references, and procedural flow can be particularly complex. The investment of time, however, in acclimating to operative report transcription can pay big dividends down the road. Once learned, operative notes lend themselves well to word expanders and templates, given their highly repetitive and predictable nature, particularly with common procedures.

Tips and Strategies for this Chapter:

- *Read the chapter thoroughly, highlighting or underlining references that are unfamiliar to you.*
- *Make index cards or quick-reference lists for the neurologic classification systems outlined in this chapter.*
- *Make index cards or quick-reference lists for anatomic terms and classification systems.*
- *Begin a list of common surgical equipment terms to use as a reference while transcribing operative reports.*
- *Familiarize yourself with the chapter index found in the margin on the first page of this chapter in your BOS (page 381) and practice navigating the chapter using the index.*

Exam Prep Assessment

Apply your understanding and knowledge of Chapter 18 to the multiple-choice exam prep questions below.

1. A Glasgow coma score of 7 or less indicates what level of consciousness?

   A. normal
   B. functional
   C. coma
   D. brain death

2. Cranial nerve 10 is the ____________ nerve.

   A. optic
   B. vagus
   C. olfactory
   D. facial

3. There are _________ cervical spinal nerves.

   A. 5
   B. 12
   C. 7
   D. 8

4. Which is expressed correctly?

   A. 0.062 K-wire
   B. 0.062 K wire
   C. 0.62 K-wire
   D. 0.62 K-wire

5. The vertical plane dividing the body into right and left portions is called the _____________ plane.

   A. frontal
   B. sagittal
   C. transverse
   D. axial

6. All of these represent the correct and/or acceptable expression of a term *except:*

   A. crepitus.

B. fingerbreadths.
C. fluctuance.
D. crepitants.

7. A grading of +2 indicates reflexes that are:

A. absent.
B. decreased.
C. normal.
D. hyperactive.

8. The Neer-Horowitz system classifies:

A. proximal humeral physeal fractures in children.
B. damage in chondromalacia patellae.
C. tibial plateau fractures.
D. developmental dysplasia of the hip.

9. The severity of Legg-Perthes disease (pediatric avascular necrosis of the femoral head) is classified as score/grade of:

A. I through IV.
B. I through III.
C. 1 through 4.
D. I through IIIB.

10. The vestibulocochlear nerve is referred to by which number?

A. 3
B. 6
C. 8
D. 11

11. Which is expressed correctly?

A. There was exquisite tenderness on palpation of the T1, 2, and 3 spinous processes.
B. X-ray revealed degenerative disk disease at L5/S1.
C. She had permanent fusion of C3-C4-C5.

D. The patient had minimally invasive bilateral resection of L-4 lamina for intradural spinal cord tumor.

12. In EEG reporting, *A1* and *A2* refer to:

A. earlobe electrodes.
B. central electrodes.
C. occipital electrodes.
D. parietal electrodes.

13. On the Rancho Los Amigos cognitive function scale, a patient with confused and agitated behavior would be assessed which classification level?

A. II
B. III
C. IV
D. V

14. In the neurologic test for *SSEP,* the *EP* refers to:

A. elicited paroxysm.
B. electrode placement.
C. evoked potentials.
D. electrical patterns.

15. All of the following are systems used to classify fractures *except:*

A. Garden.
B. LeFort.
C. Salter-Harris.
D. Outerbridge.

Proofreading/Editing

Correct the errors in each of the sentences below.

1. Deep tendon reflexes were bilaterally symmetrical, with upper extremities 1-2+/2 and lower extremities 2+/2.

2. The drill bit was removed, and a two-four 8-10 mm Osteomed screw was placed in the area.

3. There was gross instability of the left medio-collateral ligament and anterior cruciate ligament with a positive McMurray's maneuver to suggest an O'Donoghue's Triad.

4. There was no evidence of fracture on plane films.

5. The patient fell down a flight of steps and sustained a Garden stage two femoral neck fracture.

6. DIAGNOSIS: Neer stage 2 shoulder.

7. The osteotomy site was fixed via the use of a 45 Kirschner wire.

8. DIAGNOSIS: Subluxation, L-5/S-1.

9. There was an area of tenderness 3 fingersbreadth below the umbilicus.

10. X-ray revealed a type two B fracture of the olecranon.

Answer Key—Chapter 18

Refer to the answer keys below for answers to practical application exercises for this chapter.

Exam Prep Assessment

1. C
2. B
3. D
4. A
5. B
6. D
7. C
8. A
9. A
10. C

11. C
12. A
13. C
14. C
15. D

Proofreading/Editing

1. Deep tendon reflexes were bilaterally symmetrical, with upper extremities 1+/2 to 2+/2 and lower extremities 2+/2.
2. The drill bit was removed, and a 2.4/8-10 mm Osteomed screw was placed in the area.
3. There was gross instability of the left medial collateral ligament and anterior cruciate ligament with a positive McMurray maneuver to suggest an O'Donoghue triad.
4. There was no evidence of fracture on plain films.
5. The patient fell down a flight of steps and sustained a Garden stage 2 femoral neck fracture.
6. DIAGNOSIS: Neer stage II shoulder.
7. The osteotomy site was fixed via the use of a 0.045 Kirschner wire.
8. DIAGNOSIS: Subluxation, L5-S1.
9. There was an area of tenderness 3 fingerbreadths below the umbilicus.
10. X-ray revealed a type IIB fracture of the olecranon.

Transcription Practice

Complete the Transcription Practice exercises for Chapter 18 on the CD-ROM included with this text. Answers to these exercises can be found in Appendix A at the back of this book.

CHAPTER 19

Obstetrics Gynecology Pediatrics

Learning objectives for this chapter:

- ✓ Understand and apply *Book of Style* (BOS) standards related to obstetrics and gynecology.
- ✓ Understand and apply *Book of Style* (BOS) standards related to pediatrics.
- ✓ Accurately identify these standards via multiple-choice questions that prepare you for AHDI credentialing examinations.
- ✓ Apply your knowledge of these standards to proofreading/editing exercises that will prepare you for practical application in the workplace and on AHDI credentialing examinations.
- ✓ Apply your knowledge of these standards in a simulated work setting through transcription of sample dictation clips designed to test the standards outlined in this chapter.

Introduction

This chapter is a relatively short, focused orientation to a common but unique specialty that most MTs will encounter in the field, either in a specialty practice or in acute care, as virtually every large hospital (and most small ones) has labor, delivery, and neonatal departments—although the latter is often not found in small or rural facilities. In high-risk pregnancies, women are often directed to a larger hospital with an adequate neonatal facility.

In the gynecologic setting, an MT will encounter terminology, tests, and diagnoses related to vaginal, cervical, and uterine health as well as those that pertain to the ovulatory cycle, hormone regulation, and infertility. It is important to remember that this also includes the evolving reproductive health of women as they approach and transition through menopause. Orientation to specialty equipment (tenaculums, uterine sounds, clamps, etc.) and operative terms (Pfannenstiel, cerclage, etc.) will also be critical in your preparation for an acute-care exposure to this specialty.

Tips and Strategies for this Chapter:

- *Read the chapter thoroughly, highlighting or underlining references that are unfamiliar to you.*
- *Make index cards or quick-reference lists for the classification systems outlined in this chapter.*
- *Make index cards or quick-reference lists for L&D stages and gravida/para delineations.*
- *Familiarize yourself with the chapter index found in the margin on the first page of this chapter in your BOS (page 401) and practice navigating the chapter using the index.*

Exam Prep Assessment

Apply your understanding and knowledge of Chapter 19 to the multiple-choice exam prep questions below.

1. Female breasts reach mature adult size at Tanner stage:

   A. 2
   B. 3
   C. 4
   D. 5

2. Normal karyotype for males is:

   A. 46,XX
   B. 46,XY

C. 45,X
D. 47,XXY

3. Which represents the correct transcription of the dictated excerpt below?

DICTATED: At six hours into labor, she was six ninety minus three.

A. At 6 hours into labor, she was 690 minus 3.
B. At 6 hours into labor, she was 6, 90, -3.
C. At 6 hours into labor, she was 6 cm, 90%, and -3.
D. At 6 hours into labor, she was 6 cm, 90%, minus 3.

4. FIGO stages carcinoma of the ovary from:

A. I to IV.
B. 1 to 4.
C. I to V.
D. 1 to 5.

5. Which of these is *not* evaluated on Apgar testing of a newborn?

A. pulse
B. cry
C. color
D. reflex

6. Chromosomes 6-12 and X are in which genetic group?

A. A
B. B
C. C
D. D

7. All of these are used to classify cervical cytology *except:*

A. POP-Q classification.
B. Papanicolau testing.
C. CIN classification.
D. Bethesda system.

8. Which is correct?

   A. Apgars were 8/9 at 1/5.
   B. Apgars were 8 and 9 at 1 and 5 minutes.
   C. Apgar scores were 8 and 9 at one and five minutes.
   D. Apgar scores were 8 and 9 at 1 and 5 minutes.

9. On POP-Q assessment, the patient is given a stage classification of:

   A. 1 to 4.
   B. I to IV.
   C. Zero to 4.
   D. Zero to IV.

10. A nulliparous patient has had:

    A. zero pregnancies.
    B. multiple pregnancies.
    C. zero viable births.
    D. multiple viable births.

11. What is the *minimum* number of times a para 2-1-0-3 patient has been pregnant?

    A. 1
    B. 2
    C. 3
    D. 4

12. There are ________ distinct stages of labor.

    A. 2
    B. 3
    C. 4
    D. 6

13. Which is correct?

    A. Right adnexa is normal.
    B. BUS is normal.
    C. Adnexa are normal.
    D. BUS glands are normal.

14. A patient with an obstetrical history of *3-0-0-2* has had:

    A. 3 term births and 2 abortions.
    B. 3 term births with 2 living children.
    C. 3 pregnancies and 2 live births.
    D. 3 premature births and 2 term births.

15. An ASCUS finding is reported under which classification system?

    A. Bethesda
    B. Papanicolau
    C. CIN
    D. FIGO

Proofreading/Editing

Correct the errors in each of the sentences below.

1. She is gravida-2, para-1, ab-2, and her last menstrual period was in 1958.

2. PREOPERATIVE DIAGNOSIS: Previous Cesarean section.

3. A live female newborn, Apgars 99 at 1 and 5 minutes, weight 4310 gm, was delivered.

4. On examination, the adnexae were normal.

5. We discussed her FIGO stage 3B ovarian carcinoma as well as her long-term prognosis.

6. The remaining 48 cells were of normal female karyotype 46-XX.

7. She was 80% effaced with cervix dilated to 4 cm, and the fetus was noted to be at minus 2 station.

8. This is a G3/P2-1-0-3 female who presents today with vaginal bleeding.

9. She delivered a female weighing 8 lb 5 oz and sustained a fourth degree laceration.

10. Obstetrical history: Gravida 4, para 3-0-1-4.

Answer Key—Chapter 19

Refer to the answer keys below for answers to practical application exercises for this chapter.

Exam Prep Assessment

1. D
2. B
3. C
4. A
5. B
6. C
7. A
8. C
9. B
10. C
11. B
12. B
13. C
14. B
15. A

Proofreading/Editing

1. She is gravida 2, para 1, ab 2, and her last menstrual period was in 1958.

2. PREOPERATIVE DIAGNOSIS: Previous cesarean section.

3. A live female newborn, Apgars 9 and 9 at one and five minutes, weight 4310 g, was delivered.

4. On examination, the adnexa were normal.

5. We discussed her FIGO stage IIIb ovarian carcinoma as well as her long-term prognosis.

6. The remaining 48 cells were of normal female karyotype 46,XX.

7. She was 80% effaced with cervix dilated to 4 cm, and the fetus was noted to be at -2 station.

8. This is a G3, P2-1-0-3 female who presents today with vaginal bleeding.

9. She delivered a female weighing 8 pounds 5 ounces and sustained a 4th degree laceration.

10. Obstetrical history: Gravida 4, para 3-0-1-4.

Note: A gravida 4 female who has had 1 abortion could not have a para history that reflects 4 living children. Edit appropriately or flag to the dictator's attention.

Transcription Practice

Complete the Transcription Practice exercises for Chapter 19 on the CD-ROM included with this text. Answers to these exercises can be found in Appendix A at the back of this book.

CHAPTER 20

Ophthalmology

Learning objectives for this chapter:

- ✓ Understand and apply *Book of Style* (BOS) standards related to evaluation and diagnostic terms for ophthalmology.
- ✓ Understand and apply *Book of Style* (BOS) standards related to testing and equipment for ophthalmology/optometry.
- ✓ Understand and apply *Book of Style* (BOS) standards related ophthalmologic classification and measuring systems.
- ✓ Accurately identify these standards via multiple-choice questions that prepare you for AHDI credentialing examinations.
- ✓ Apply your knowledge of these standards to proofreading/editing exercises that will prepare you for practical application in the workplace and on AHDI credentialing examinations.
- ✓ Apply your knowledge of these standards in a simulated work setting through transcription of sample dictation clips designed to test the standards outlined in this chapter.

Introduction

While few MTs find themselves interpreting the complex specialty of ophthalmology, certainly many working in an acute care setting will be called upon to transcribe and document surgical procedures that relate to this specialty (i.e., cataract procedures, lens implantations, etc.). The language of ophthalmology is unusual and requires specific training and exposure to more unique classification systems and assessing equipment than almost any other specialty. MTs in this domain need to be mindful of the reality that the expression of complex measurements in optometry and ophthalmology is very precise, and a thorough understanding of visual field measurements, diopter corrections, and visual acuity will be required. Numbers are rarely expressed in writing exactly as they may sound when dictated (visual acuity dictated as "21 hundred" is expressed uniquely as 20/100, for example). This is one of the many specialties where standards of expression are *very* important and matter significantly in the context of communicated care and course of treatment.

Tips and Strategies for this Chapter:

- *Read the chapter thoroughly, highlighting or underlining references that are unfamiliar to you.*
- *Familiarize yourself with the chapter index found in the margin on the first page of this chapter in your BOS (page 417) and practice navigating the chapter using the index.*

Exam Prep Assessment

Apply your understanding and knowledge of Chapter 20 to the multiple-choice exam prep questions below.

1. Which of these refers to the right eye?

   A. OR
   B. OD
   C. OS
   D. OU

2. Which is transcribed correctly?

   A. There was a cup-to-disk ratio of 0.75.
   B. Adnexa oculi is examined and found to be normal.
   C. There was an area of ischemia of approximately 2 DA.
   D. Visual acuity was 2200 OU.

3. All of these are used to measure visual acuity *except:*

   A. Snellen fractions.
   B. Goldmann system.
   C. Bailey-Lovie system.
   D. Jaeger system.

4. The logMAR unit is part of the ____________________ system.

   A. Bailey-Lovie
   B. Snellen
   C. Jaeger
   D. Goldmann

5. The power of an optical lens is measured in:

   A. degrees.
   B. fields.
   C. diopters.
   D. refractions.

6. Mass retinal response to light stimulus is measured by:

   A. electroretinogram.
   B. LOCS II.
   C. argon laser.
   D. culogram.

7. Which represents the correct transcription of the underlined portion of the sentence below?

DICTATED: Refraction was plus <u>two-fifty, plus five hundred, axis 90</u>.

   A. +250, +500, axis 90
   B. +2.50, +5.00, axis 90
   C. +.250, +.500, axis 90
   D. +0.25, +0.50, axis 90

8. The roman numerals in the Goldmann perimetry system designate:

   A. diopter power.
   B. luminance.
   C. spot size.
   D. refraction.

9. In PERG, the "P" stands for:

   A. percutaneous.
   B. pattern.
   C. pressure.
   D. pulsatile.

10. Which of these refers to each eye (or both eyes)?

   A. oculus dexter
   B. oculus sinister
   C. oculus uterque
   D. oculus ubiquiti

Proofreading/Editing

Correct the errors in each of the sentences below.

1. ASSESSMENT: Grade Nc2, N0, CTR, P2 right cataract.

2. Refraction was +200, +250, axis 90.

3. ERG shows an A wave and B wave complex separated from the D wave, which is generated at stimulus offset.

4. HEENT: There was bilateral injection of the conjunctivae on ocular examination.

5. Visual acuity was 2500 OU.

6. His near visual acuity is now J-4 plus and will require adjustment of his prescriptive reading glasses.

7. Bailey Lovie testing revealed a Logmar acuity score of 0.34.

8. He has moderate myopia requiring -5 diopter correction.

Answer Key—Chapter 20

Refer to the answer keys below for answers to practical application exercises for this chapter.

Exam Prep Assessment

1. B
2. C
3. B
4. A
5. C
6. A
7. B
8. C
9. B
10. C

Proofreading/Editing

1. ASSESSMENT: Grade NCII, N0, Ctr, PII right cataract.

2. Refraction was +2.00, +2.50, axis 90.

3. ERG shows an a-wave and b-wave complex separated from the d-wave, which is generated at stimulus offset.

4. HEENT: There was bilateral hyperemia of the conjunctivae on ocular examination.

5. Visual acuity was 20/500 OU.

6. His near visual acuity is now J4+ and will require adjustment of his prescriptive reading glasses.

7. Bailey-Lovie testing revealed a logMAR acuity score of 0.34.

8. He has moderate myopia requiring -5.00 D correction.

Transcription Practice

Complete the Transcription Practice exercises for Chapter 20 on the CD-ROM included with this text. Answers to these exercises can be found in Appendix A at the back of this book.

Organisms and Pathogens

Learning objectives for this chapter:

- ✓ Understand and apply *Book of Style* (BOS) standards related to biological nomenclature and classification structures.
- ✓ Understand and apply *Book of Style* (BOS) standards related to expression and classification of bacteria.
- ✓ Understand and apply *Book of Style* (BOS) standards related to expression and classification of viruses.
- ✓ Accurately identify these standards via multiple-choice questions that prepare you for AHDI credentialing examinations.
- ✓ Apply your knowledge of these standards to proofreading/editing exercises that will prepare you for practical application in the workplace and on AHDI credentialing examinations.
- ✓ Apply your knowledge of these standards in a simulated work setting through transcription of sample dictation clips designed to test the standards outlined in this chapter.

Introduction

Pathogenic organisms are defined as those that cause human disease. They include molecules (like proteinaceous particles) and viruses that are only visible under a high-power electron microscope; bacteria, fungi, and protozoan parasites that are sometimes visible to the naked eye; and multicellular parasites, such as tapeworms, that are large enough to be easily seen by the naked eye. Most can be found thriving in natural ecosystems, living often symbiotically with other species, and surprisingly very few require a human host for survival.

Pathogenic organisms can harm human health in several ways, such as depriving their human host of vital nutrients, producing poisonous metabolic products, destroying vital organs and tissues, or interfering with body chemistry. Their potential to wreak havoc on a human host is significant, and even more dangerous is their unpredictable impact on humans based on the virility of the organism and the immune defense of the human in which they may be introduced.

Rapid advances in microbiology and immunology have lead to greater understanding and identification of organisms as well as better diagnosis and treatment, though "superbugs" (i.e., organisms that evolve toward greater resistance to antibiotic treatment) continue to keep epidemiologists and hospitalists on their toes. There are few specialties in which an MT may be engaged that will be free of the terminology and standards of style outlined in this chapter, as every clinical specialty has to concern itself with the potential for infection. Therefore, the information in this chapter will be important for the working MT in *any* clinical setting.

Tips and Strategies for this Chapter:

- *Read the chapter thoroughly, highlighting or underlining references that are unfamiliar to you.*
- *Create lists or reference cards on which you begin to differentiate between common bacterial entities, viral entities, and parasitic entities that you will most often encounter in the health record. While there are a wide array of pathogens you will be expected to recognize and document in the record, you will find that only the most common will be regularly encountered.*
- *Make quick-reference cards outlining the taxonomic structures outlined in this chapter.*
- *Familiarize yourself with the chapter index found in the margin on the first page of this chapter in your BOS (page 423) and practice navigating the chapter using the index.*

Exam Prep Assessment

Apply your understanding and knowledge of Chapter 21 to the multiple-choice exam prep questions below.

1. The prognosis of someone with Child-Pugh class B hepatitis is:

   A. 1-2 years.
   B. 1-3 months.
   C. candidate for transplant.
   D. 15-20 years.

2. Organisms are scientifically classified in groups called:

   A. ranks.
   B. taxa.
   C. genuses.
   D. species.

3. All of the following are *formal* taxonomic terms *except:*

   A. Fungi.
   B. Staphylococcus aureus.
   C. Procaryotae.
   D. Pneumococcus.

4. Which of these is not a taxon rank?

   A. kingdom
   B. class
   C. family
   D. type

5. Which represents the accurate expression of the underlined portion of the dictated sentence below?

   DICTATED: Mom presents today seeking <u>swine flu</u> vaccinations for all 5 children.

   A. "swine flu"

B. swine flu
C. H1N1
D. "H1N1"

6. Streptococci are uniquely grouped into ___ Lancefield serologic groups.

A. 1
B. 2
C. 3
D. 4

7. Human herpesvirus 5 is more commonly known as:

A. Epstein-Barr virus.
B. cytomegalovirus.
C. HIV.
D. varicella-zoster virus.

8. The antibody to hepatitis A would be expressed in abbreviated form as:

A. anti-HAV.
B. anti-HBV.
C. AHAV.
D. AHAB.

9. All of the following are measured under the Child-Pugh scoring system for hepatitis *except:*

A. bilirubin.
B. serum albumin.
C. INR.
D. viral load.

10. Which of these refers to a drug-resistant species of bacteria?

A. HBIG
B. EHEC
C. HAV
D. MRSA

Proofreading/Editing

Correct the errors in each of the sentences below.

1. IMPRESSION: Pneumonia secondary to a long bout with H. flu in this immunocompromised patient.
2. DIAGNOSIS: Child Pugh Class C hepatitis.
3. Cultures quickly grew out strep chains.
4. Salmonella enteritidis is the most common form of salmonella in the United States.
5. Sputum for CNS and gram-stain were ordered.
6. DIAGNOSIS: HAV.
7. I counseled her about treatment regimens for her chronic Varicella zoster infection.
8. PAST MEDICAL HISTORY: Non-A/B hepatitis.
9. She preferred treatment of her Candidiasis with single-dose Diflucan.
10. The patient presents with a long history of Cytomegalovirus.

Answer Key—Chapter 21

Refer to the answer keys below for answers to practical application exercises for this chapter.

Exam Prep Assessment

1. C
2. B
3. D
4. D
5. A
6. C
7. B
8. A
9. D
10. D

Proofreading/Editing

1. IMPRESSION: Pneumonia secondary to a long bout with Haemophilus influenza in this immunocompromised patient.

2. DIAGNOSIS: Child-Pugh class C hepatitis.

3. Cultures quickly grew out streptococcal chains.

4. Salmonella Enteritidis is the most common form of Salmonella in the United States.

5. Sputum for C&S and Gram stain were ordered.

6. DIAGNOSIS: Hepatitis A virus.

7. I counseled her about treatment regimens for her chronic varicella-zoster infection.

8. PAST MEDICAL HISTORY: Non-A, non-B hepatitis.

9. She preferred treatment of her candidiasis with single-dose Diflucan.

10. The patient presents with a long history of cytomegalovirus.

Transcription Practice

Complete the Transcription Practice exercises for Chapter 21 on the CD-ROM included with this text. Answers to these exercises can be found in Appendix A at the back of this book.

Psychiatry

Learning objectives for this chapter:

- ✓ Understand and apply *Book of Style* (BOS) standards related to psychiatric terminology.
- ✓ Understand and apply *Book of Style* (BOS) standards related to classification systems for psychiatry and mental health.
- ✓ Accurately identify these standards via multiple-choice questions that prepare you for AHDI credentialing examinations.
- ✓ Apply your knowledge of these standards to proofreading/editing exercises that will prepare you for practical application in the workplace and on AHDI credentialing examinations.
- ✓ Apply your knowledge of these standards in a simulated work setting through transcription of sample dictation clips designed to test the standards outlined in this chapter.

Introduction

The term "mental health" has a broad implication in health care. It can refer to an acute state of illness that requires complex psychiatric testing and analysis, or it can simply refer to the mental status of a patient who is coping with the impact of a terminal illness, debilitating disease, or loss of quality of life. Clinicians are increasingly more mindful of a patient's mental well-being in the presence of acute or chronic illness and many are proactively evaluating mental status as part of ongoing treatment and care planning for their patients. Many common illnesses, such as sleep disorders, can be erroneously attributed to physiology when a compromise of mental status, such as is seen in depression, could be the real contributory culprit. An assessment of perception, ideology, and sense of well-being are critical not only to diagnosis but to predicting the degree to which the patient will be compliant with therapy or responsive to rehabilitation. Patients who emerge from cardiac bypass surgery, for example, are now monitored closely for signs of depression that could interfere with a patient's willingness to make lifestyle changes and participate in necessary rehabilitation.

Then there are those patients, of course, who present with acute compromise of mental status, and the MT working in the field of psychiatric medicine will be exposed to a diverse field of diagnosis and treatment whose language and expression is highly unique and descriptive. Even for the MT who encounters psychiatric reference only occasionally in the mix of other acute care dictation will need to be familiar with this complex and dynamic specialty.

Tips and Strategies for this Chapter:

- *Read the chapter thoroughly, highlighting or underlining references that are unfamiliar to you.*
- *Add the classification systems encountered in this chapter to your quick-reference list of classification systems; include a description, the standard for correct expression, and the specialty associated with the system.*
- *Make a quick-reference card for psychiatric diagnosis Axis delineations.*
- *Familiarize yourself with the chapter index found in the margin on the first page of this chapter in your BOS (page 435) and practice navigating the chapter using the index.*

Exam Prep Assessment

Apply your understanding and knowledge of Chapter 22 to the multiple-choice exam prep questions below.

1. A patient's general medical conditions would be reported under which of these on psychiatric assessment?

   A. Axis I
   B. Axis II
   C. Axis III
   D. Axis IV

2. What manual for classifying psychiatric illness is published by the American Psychiatric Association?

   A. Diagnostic Manual for Mental Assessment
   B. Diagnostic and Statistical Manual of Mental Disorders
   C. Psychiatric Diagnosis and Assessment Manual
   D. Manual for Clinical Diagnosis of the Psychiatric Patient

3. The AMA Manual of Style recommends which word be substituted in place of the word *manic*?

   A. hyperactive
   B. bipolar
   C. overactive
   D. frenetic

4. Which of these is _not_ assessed as part of a mental status exam?

   A. appearance
   B. memory
   C. judgment
   D. neurologic function

5. The maximum score on the Mini-Mental State Examination is:

   A. 30
   B. 20
   C. 15
   D. 10

6. *GAF* refers to:

   A. General Assessment of Functioning.
   B. Global Assessment of Functioning.
   C. General Acuity Factor.
   D. Global Acuity Factor.

7. Which of these is used to assess *personality*?

   A. Rorschach Test
   B. Myers-Briggs Assessment
   C. Zung Scale
   D. Hamilton Scale

8. *SOFAS* measures social-occupational functioning on a scale of:

   A. 0 to 5.
   B. 0 to 10.
   C. 0 to 20.
   D. 0 to 100.

9. GAF is reported under which axis on psychiatric assessment?

   A. I
   B. II
   C. IV
   D. V

10. A patient's history of drug abuse would be reported under which axis on psychiatric assessment?

   A. I
   B. II
   C. IV
   D. V

Proofreading/Editing

Correct the errors in each of the sentences below.

1. DIAGNOSIS:

Axis I	Clinical depression.
Axis II	Diabetes mellitus and hyperlipidemia.
Axis III	Recently separated from his spouse.
Axis IV	Current GAF 70.

2. Monumental status score was 23.

3. The patient appeared to be completely catatonic on my initial examination.

4. DIAGNOSIS:

Axis I	PTSD (309.81).
Axis II	Avoidant personality disorder (301.82).
Axis III	None.
Axis IV	Unemployed; marital stress.
Axis V	GAF 60 (current); blunt affect.

5. She appeared to be high-functioning, with sofas of 80 on evaluation.

Answer Key—Chapter 22

Refer to the answer keys below for answers to practical application exercises for this chapter.

Exam Prep Assessment

1. C
2. B
3. C
4. D
5. A
6. B
7. B
8. D
9. D
10. A

Proofreading/Editing

1. DIAGNOSIS:

Axis I		Clinical depression.
Axis II		None.
Axis III		Diabetes mellitus and hyperlipidemia.
Axis IV		Recently separated from his spouse.
Axis V		Current GAF 70.

2. Mini-Mental State Examination score was 23.

3. The patient appeared to be completely motionless on my initial examination.

4. DIAGNOSIS:

Axis I	309.81	Posttraumatic stress disorder (PTSD).
Axis II	301.82	Avoidant personality disorder.
Axis III		None.
Axis IV		Unemployed; marital stress.
Axis V		GAF 60 (current); blunt affect.

5. She appeared to be high-functioning, with SOFAS of 80 on evaluation.

Transcription Practice

Complete the Transcription Practice exercises for Chapter 22 on the CD-ROM included with this text. Answers to these exercises can be found in Appendix A at the back of this book.

Pulmonary Respiratory

Learning objectives for this chapter:

- ✓ Understand and apply *Book of Style* (BOS) standards related to pulmonary and respiratory terms.
- ✓ Understand and apply *Book of Style* (BOS) standards related to accurate expression of diagnostic and treatment terms in pulmonary and respiratory medicine.
- ✓ Understand and apply *Book of Style* (BOS) standards related to classification systems encountered in these specialties.
- ✓ Accurately identify these standards via multiple-choice questions that prepare you for AHDI credentialing examinations.
- ✓ Apply your knowledge of these standards to proofreading/editing exercises that will prepare you for practical application in the workplace and on AHDI credentialing examinations.
- ✓ Apply your knowledge of these standards in a simulated work setting through transcription of sample dictation clips designed to test the standards outlined in this chapter.

Introduction

As outlined in the opening of this chapter in the *Book of Style,* the unique terminology, diagnostic studies, and classification systems found in pulmonary medicine are likely to be encountered across a broad spectrum of clinic settings, both inpatient and outpatient. Assessment and management of pulmonary function as well as short- and long-term management of a patient's need for mechanical ventilation are likely to be referenced quite frequently in an acute care setting, but it is also likely that the MT providing documentation services to a cardiology, infectious disease, pediatric, or oncology practice (as well as most others) is also going to encounter these references, since respiratory function can be compromised and/or at risk with a great number of diseases and syndromes.

In addition, MTs are likely to encounter increasingly frequent references to polysomnography, given the emerging commonality of sleep disorders, hypopneas, and apneas that can now be readily assessed through monitored sleep studies. Familiarity with the scope and nature of testing, as well as the classification or scoring systems associated with reporting the findings of those tests, will be essential to the MT in those settings.

Tips and Strategies for this Chapter:

- *Read the chapter thoroughly, highlighting or underlining references that are unfamiliar to you.*
- *Add the classification systems encountered in this chapter to your quick-reference list of classification systems; include a description, the standard for correct expression, and the specialty associated with the system.*
- *Reference the normal value ranges for typical pulmonary/respiratory testing, i.e., arterial blood gases and PFTs, and make it a point to memorize those normal values, which will predispose you to recognize errors and/or discrepancies in the record and prepare you for advanced editing.*
- *Familiarize yourself with the chapter index found in the margin on the first page of this chapter in your BOS (page 441) and practice navigating the chapter using the index.*

Exam Prep Assessment

Apply your understanding and knowledge of Chapter 23 to the multiple-choice exam prep questions below.

1. *PEEP* refers to:

   A. pulmonary endotracheal expiratory pressure.
   B. positive endotracheal expiratory pressure.
   C. positive end-expiratory pressure.
   D. pulmonary end-expiratory pressure.

2. Which is expressed correctly?

   A. 3 liters of O2
   B. 3 l of O2
   C. 3 L of O2
   D. 3L of O2

3. Which of these is *not* a physiologic parameter that is monitored during polysomnography?

   A. ECMO
   B. EOG
   C. EEG
   D. EMG

4. The primary gas phase symbol *Q* refers to:

   A. specific conductance.
   B. volume of blood.
   C. resistance.
   D. volume of gas.

5. Which is transcribed correctly?

   A. Respirations were 22/min.
   B. Respirations were 22 per min.
   C. Respirations: 22/min
   D. Respirations: 22 bpm

6. A score of *2* on the Epworth Sleepiness Scale represents a patient who:

   A. would never doze or sleep.
   B. has a slight chance of dozing or sleeping.
   C. has a moderate chance of dozing or sleeping.
   D. has a high chance of dozing or sleeping.

7. Which Epworth Sleepiness Scale total score below would be likely in a patient with *severe sleepiness*?

   A. 10
   B. 14
   C. 18
   D. 23

8. The Mallampati-Samsoon classification system is used to:

   A. assess airway for ease of intubation.
   B. measure daytime sleepiness in the assessment of sleep disorders.
   C. determine likelihood of depression in patients with potential sleep disorders.
   D. assess pulmonary function and the need for mechanical ventilation.

9. *FEV* is measured as part of:

   A. arterial blood gases.
   B. pulmonary function testing.
   C. mechanical ventilation.
   D. polysomnography.

10. A patient in whom assessment of the airway indicates that only the faucial pillars and soft palate can be visualized would be classified as class ___________ under the Mallampati-Samsoon system.

    A. I
    B. II
    C. III
    D. IV

Proofreading/Editing

Correct the errors in each of the sentences below.

1. Arterial blood gases revealed Po2 and PCo2 to be within normal limits.
2. Blood pressure was 121/72, with respirations at 22/min.
3. FEV1:FVC was 40% of predicted.
4. The patient was placed on BIPAP ventilator support.
5. EMS reported the patient had a class 4 airway, and tracheotomy was performed in the field.

Answer Key—Chapter 23

Refer to the answer keys below for answers to practical application exercises for this chapter.

Exam Prep Assessment

1. C
2. D
3. A
4. B
5. C
6. C
7. C
8. A
9. B
10. B

Proofreading/Editing

1. Arterial blood gases revealed pO2 and pCO2 to be within normal limits.
2. Blood pressure was 121/72, with respirations at 22 per minute.
3. FEV1-FVC was 40% of predicted.
4. The patient was placed on BiPAP ventilator support.

5. EMS reported the patient had a class IV airway, and tracheotomy was performed in the field.

Transcription Practice

Complete the Transcription Practice exercises for Chapter 23 on the CD-ROM included with this text. Answers to these exercises can be found in Appendix A at the back of this book.

CHAPTER 24

Other Specialty Standards

Learning objectives for this chapter:

- ✓ Understand and apply *Book of Style* (BOS) standards related to radiology terms and classification systems.
- ✓ Understand and apply *Book of Style* (BOS) standards related to diabetes mellitus terms and classification systems.
- ✓ Understand and apply *Book of Style* (BOS) standards related to molecular terms and classification systems.
- ✓ Accurately identify these standards via multiple-choice questions that prepare you for AHDI credentialing examinations.
- ✓ Apply your knowledge of these standards to proofreading/editing exercises that will prepare you for practical application in the workplace and on AHDI credentialing examinations.
- ✓ Apply your knowledge of these standards in a simulated work setting through transcription of sample dictation clips designed to test the standards outlined in this chapter.

Introduction

This final chapter addressed several standards of style and expression that did not fit well into other sections of this text but are important enough (and likely to be frequently encountered by the working healthcare documentation specialist) to warrant their inclusion in this book. However, because there are only three short sections in this chapter, there are fewer practice questions and exercises than you have encountered in previous chapters of this workbook.

Tips and Strategies for this Chapter:

- *Read the chapter thoroughly, highlighting or underlining references that are unfamiliar to you.*
- *Familiarize yourself with the chapter index found in the margin on the first page of this chapter in your BOS (page 451) and practice navigating the chapter using the index.*

Exam Prep Assessment

Apply your understanding and knowledge of Chapter 24 to the multiple-choice exam prep questions below.

1. *Adult-onset diabetes* is now classified as type ________ diabetes.

   A. 1
   B. 2
   C. 3
   D. 4

2. Which refers to the measure of intensity and timing of diffusion gradient in diffusion-weighted MRIs?

   A. relaxation time
   B. echo train
   C. k-space
   D. b value

3. Which is transcribed correctly?

   A. β galactosidase activity
   B. BCL2 gene

C. cDNA blunting
D. CPG nucleotide

4. A pregnant woman with diabetic nephropathy has which class of gestational diabetes?

   A. C
   B. D
   C. E
   D. F

5. Which is correct?

   A. We requested his previous x-rays.
   B. He was sent down to x-ray for repeat films.
   C. I believe we will need to re-x-ray the right wrist.
   D. The patient was x-ray'd at the bedside.

6. Which is expressed correctly?

   A. Imaging of the coronary lumen and vessel-wall was performed using MRI with a radial K-space trajectory at 3 T.
   B. MRI acquisition included a DT-MRI scan with 6 mm axial slices and maximum b factor of 1044 s/sq mm.
   C. An echotrain length between 3 and 16 is typically selected for evaluation of connective tissue.
   D. Via MRI, we measured the T-1 and T-2 relaxation times of cartilage, synovial fluid, muscle, marrow, and fat at 1.5 and 3.0 T.

7. All of these are third-class classifications of diabetes mellitus *except:*

   A. gestational.
   B. genetic defects of beta-cell function.
   C. endocrinopathies.
   D. drug- or chemical-induced.

8. Which refers to diabetes that is caused by beta-cell destruction?

   A. Type 1
   B. Type 2
   C. Third-class
   D. Gestational

9. Pregnant women with class A, B, or C gestational diabetes are likely to have babies that are:

   A. born prematurely.
   B. small for gestational age.
   C. large for gestational age.
   D. born with impaired glucose tolerance.

10. *Juvenile diabetes* is now classified as:

   A. type 2 child.
   B. type 1 adult.
   C. type 1 child.
   D. type 3.

Answer Key—Chapter 24

Refer to the answer key below for answers to the practical application exercise for this chapter.

Exam Prep Assessment

1. B
2. D
3. C
4. D
5. A
6. B
7. A
8. A
9. C
10. C

Transcription Practice

Complete the Transcription Practice exercises for Chapter 24 on the CD-ROM included with this text. Answers to these exercises can be found in Appendix A at the back of this book.

Appendix A
CD-ROM Transcription Practice Answer Keys

Chapter 6—Punctuation

1. She also states that she is intolerant of Tylenol; however, she takes Anacin-3, which is 500 mg of acetaminophen with 32 mg of caffeine, and takes 2 tablets p.o. t.i.d. or q.i.d. for relief.

2. He has had an IVP done, the results of which are unknown.

3. His abdomen is nontender, and he has hepatomegaly, with liver span being approximately 10 cm below the right costal margin.

4. We then raised flaps, incising the scarred anoderm off the underlying internal sphincter, coming around to the directly lateral position, at which point a partial sphincterotomy was performed.

5. This is a 33-year-old Caucasian male who was involved in an MVA, possibly a motorcycle accident, early on the morning of admission.

6. The appendix was clamped, tied, and divided in routine fashion, with the stump inverted and ligated in place.

7. When questioned about her attempted suicide, she said, "God told me to do it."

8. With the erythema, shocklike state, and no explanation for the fever, ANA studies were done, which were positive at 1:160 of the speckled type.

9. Of note, the patient had evidence of ethanol withdrawal, as he was quite incoherent, confused, had tachycardia, and was quite febrile.

10. She is a very well educated and articulate female who came today with well-researched questions related to her condition.

11. He had a long discussion with his lawyer about the restrictions of the attorney-client privilege.

12. He presented with neck and shoulder pain after two days of football drills that were particularly hard hitting.

13. X-rays revealed mild-to-moderate degenerative disease of the shoulder.

14. After 1 hour and 22 minutes of cross-clamp time, the patient was weaned off cardiopulmonary bypass.

15. There was an approximately 3- to 4-inch irregularly shaped scar across the right upper chest.

Chapter 7—Capitalization

1. Upon arrival to the emergency room, the patient stated that he "slipped on the ice and fell down on the sidewalk."

2. The specimen was sent for culture and Gram stain.

3. She does not report any recent change in mood (her husband seemed to concur).

4. PAST SURGICAL HISTORY: De Quervain release in 1995.

5. The patient was found to be positive for H pylori.

6. Apparently, she has recently been on Nembutal Sodium, but her sister reports that the patient has been noncompliant with this.

7. Her culture grew out gram-positive cocci.

8. This is a 26-year-old gay, Filipino man who has been HIV-positive for about 4 years.

9. He just completed his bachelor's degree in sociology and plans to work on his master's.

10. The patient will follow up with my physician assistant in 2 weeks.

Chapter 8—Plurals and Possessives

1. Repeat films showed increased narrowing of the neural foramina.
2. Babinski's were down-going on reflex testing.
3. I could tell that the patient had been strongly influenced by her daughters-in-law's clinical advice, as apparently both of her daughters-in-law are registered nurses.
4. EKG revealed P's to be upright and normal in I, II, and aVF.
5. She was admitted for bilateral reduction mammoplasty.
6. We admitted this 31-year-old white female at 38 weeks' gestation for scheduled C-section due to placenta previa.
7. I will be referring her to Dr. Anderson's and Dr. Covington's practice for surgical evaluation.
8. DIFFERENTIAL DIAGNOSIS: Discoid meniscus versus torn meniscus.
9. Serial EKGs showed progressive widening of her QRS complex.
10. She brought up the subject of her son's measles, which is particularly worrisome to her since she is 10 weeks' pregnant.

Chapter 9—Abbreviations

1. MEDICATIONS: Lanoxin 0.125 mg.
2. Examination of the eye revealed an approximately 2 mm corneal laceration.
3. DISCHARGE DIAGNOSIS: Chronic obstructive pulmonary disease (COPD).
4. Stool cultures grew out E coli after 36 hours.
5. Her EKG showed multiple PVCs.

6. We will discontinue the patient's hydrochlorothiazide for the time being and see her again in a week.

7. She will return in approximately 3 weeks for followup.

8. DIAGNOSIS: Pneumonia secondary to HIV.

9. She is to take Tylenol b.i.d. for the next 48 hours and p.r.n. thereafter.

10. INTRAVENOUS FLUIDS: Lactated Ringer solution, 500 mL.

Chapter 10—Numbers

1. SOCIAL HISTORY: He smokes 2-1/2 packs per day.

2. He will be seen in my office in 3 weeks for further followup.

3. The wound was dressed with three 4 x 4 bandages.

4. There have been several hundred cases of this flu reported in the last 2 months.

5. There was abnormal activity in leads II and III on her admitting EKG.

6. She began having complications in her 4th month of pregnancy.

7. Her tumor is grade 3 by Broders index.

8. On inspection of the patella, there was loss of articular cartilage at the 2-o'clock and 7-o'clock positions.

9. The patient sustained a gunshot wound from a .38-caliber bullet.

10. She was admitted to the emergency room at 2230 hours after transport by ambulance.

Chapter 11—Percents, Proportions, Ratios, and Ranges

1. The child was sent home to take albuterol liquid 2 mg/5 mL.

2. There is a 2:1 ratio of hydrogen to oxygen in a single water molecule.

3. She was running temperatures in the 99 to 101.5 range.

4. We gave him a 0.25% albumin injection to help boost his blood volume levels.

5. Over the course of her admission, blood pressure stayed in the 75-85 over 130-140 range.

6. We injected 0.5% Xylocaine in 1:200,000 epinephrine for local anesthesia.

7. The doses for Effexor range from 25 to 100 mg.

8. Her BUN-to-creatinine was 20:1, indicating significant dehydration.

9. There was ST elevation in leads V1 through V5.

or

There was ST elevation in Leads V_1 through V_5.

10. She has some subluxation at the C6-7 level.

Chapter 12—Units of Measure

1. The patient then had inducible ventricular fibrillation with a 15 J shock.

2. The patient's BSA was capped at 2 m^2 [*or* sq m] and the initial dose was reduced by 20%.

3. We will start Cytoxan 400 mg/m^2 plus vincristine 2 mg/m^2 and prednisone 60 mg IV on day 1 for 3 weeks.

or

We will start Cytoxan 400 mg/sq m plus vincristine 2 mg/sq m and prednisone 60 mg IV on day 1 for 3 weeks.

4. ESTIMATED BLOOD LOSS: Approximately 150 mL.

5. The patient received 1 g of Ancef prior to surgery.

6. The cervix was dilated with progressive dilators to accommodate a 7 mm suction curette.

7. A dose of 15 mCi of fluorine 19 was infused.

8. Additionally, a 28 Hz tuning fork examination was performed to test proprioception.

9. An examination under anesthesia revealed a smooth, benign prostate of approximately 30 to 35 g with no palpable masses.

10. On the right side where there was more fat, 1 minute and 28 seconds of ultrasonic liposuction was used to remove a total of 375 mL.

Chapter 13—Pharmacology

1. Initial electrolytes revealed sodium 130, chloride 99, potassium 4, and bicarbonate 12.

2. The patient will be discharged on Norpace 150 mg q.6 h., Procardia 20 mg q.6 h., and Benadryl 50 mg q.5 h. to q.6 h.

3. The patient was placed on Ventolin 0.25 mL in 3 mL of normal saline by nebulizer q.4 h.

4. She will be given Garamycin drops 3 mg/mL to be applied to the right eye b.i.d.

5. The study was performed on a portable basis following intravenous injection of 5.3 mCi of TC 99m.

or

The study was performed on a portable basis following intravenous injection of 5.3 mCi of ^{99m}TC.

6. Participants in the study were treated with iridium 192 brachytherapy.

7. Given the relapsing status of her MS, the patient was started on interferon beta-1a.

8. DISCHARGE MEDICATIONS: Glucotrol 10 mg p.o. q.a.m., Xanax 1 mg p.o. t.i.d. p.r.n., and allopurinol 100 mg p.o. daily.

9. The chemical formula for magnesium sulfate is MgSO4.

or

The chemical formula for magnesium sulfate is $MgSO_4$.

10. Her medications include 10 mg of Inderal 4 times a day, Lasix 40 mg every other day, and Isordil 10 mg four times a day.

or

Her medications include 10 mg of Inderal q.i.d., Lasix 40 mg every other day, and Isordil 10 mg q.i.d.

Chapter 14—Cardiology

1. A followup electrocardiogram done the second hospital day was considered normal, with nonspecific ST and T-wave changes in the inferior leads.

2. Blood gas analysis done on room air showed a pO2 of 63, pH 7.42, pCO2 44, and actual bicarbonate of 28.2.

or

Blood gas analysis done on room air showed a pO_2 of 63, pH 7.45, PCO_2 44, and actual bicarbonate of 28.2.

3. EKG revealed a normal sinus rhythm with ST elevation and Q waves in the inferior leads, with a reciprocal ST depression in aVL and in leads V2 through V4.

or

EKG revealed a normal sinus rhythm with ST elevation and Q waves in the inferior leads, with reciprocal ST depression in aVL and in leads V_2 through V_4.

4. Heart has normal S1 and S2 with a grade 1/6 systolic ejection murmur.

5. She has a regular rhythm with a loud 3/6 to-and-fro systolic-diastolic murmur heard over the entire precordium.

6. The threshold for ventricular capture was 0.91 volts and 1.9 mA, resistance was 580 ohms at 5 volts, and the R wave measured 5.6 mV.

7. EKG shows poor R-wave progression in V1 through V3 consistent with an old transmural infarction of the anteroseptal myocardium.

8. There were minor nondiagnostic ST-T changes as well.

9. A poststent angiogram revealed 0% residual, no evidence of dissection, TIMI-3 flow, and a closing ACT of 330 seconds.

10. The patient was diagnosed with class IV CHF.

Chapter 15—Genetics

1. Genetic testing showed substitution mutation of 4p16.3, confirming achondroplasia, as expected.

2. Using a genetic model, I demonstrated the structure of 47,XX+21 to the mother of this newly diagnosed Down's baby.

3. Though there are no truly reliable tests for Alzheimer disease, if a patient has dementia, presence of APOE*E4 may indicate an increased likelihood that the dementia is due to Alzheimer's.

4. She requested genetic testing, but I explained that since less than 1% of the US population carries a BRCA-1 or BRCA-2 mutation, screening is not typically recommended for the general population.

5. Two of 50, or 4%, of the cells examined were monosomy X (45,X).

Chapter 16—Hematology/Oncology

1. Initial lab work revealed a CBC with hemoglobin of 14.8, hematocrit of 44.6, and WBC 4200. Sodium was 130, chloride 99, potassium 4, and bicarbonate 12.

2. Sputum Gram stain showed many wbc's [*or WBCs*] and epithelial cells, many gram-positive cocci and gram-positive rods, moderate gram-negative rods, and a few gram-negative diplococci.

3. Urinalysis revealed specific gravity of 1.030.

4. PREOPERATIVE DIAGNOSIS: T2cNXM0 prostate cancer.

5. This is a 60-year-old male with a Gleason score of 4+3=7.

6. Pathology revealed this to be modified Dukes stage C2 with metastasis to the lymph nodes.

7. The patient's T3 was 147, free T4 was 7, and TSH was 1.2.

8. On the Broders index, this tumor is a grade 3.

9. We will evaluate her for HLA-B8 and HLA-Dw3, as both of these have been linked to Sjogren syndrome as well as Graves.

10. We will evaluate her immunoglobulins to determine if this could be an IgA or IgM multiple myeloma. An IgE myeloma is possible, but unlikely.

Chapter 17—Dermatology/Allergy/Immunology

1. DIAGNOSIS: T2N1M0 malignant melanoma, Breslow depth of 3 mm, Clark IV.

2. Given the complex 3rd degree burn radius sustained to approximately half of each arm, the patient has a total body burn percentage of 9%.

3. Eight of the nine D-type gastric adenocarcinomas invading the muscularis propria and subserosa had a large number of CD34+ stromal cells in the tumor stroma.

4. Four days into a course of oral amoxicillin for an ear infection, this infant developed a widespread asymptomatic morbilliform rash.

5. Dermatoscopy shows a steel-blue homogenous area with spike-like extensions characteristic of a blue nevus.

6. There were multiple condylomata acuminata on the vulva and anus.

7. Administration of IgG by the subcutaneous route is effective and safe and overcomes obstacles encountered with the use of IVIG [*or* IVIg] in some patients.

8. I have explained to the patient that recombinant interferon alfa-2a, recombinant interferon alfa-2b, and interferon alfa-n1 are indicated for treatment of hairy cell leukemia.

9. The helper/inducer to suppressor/cytotoxic T-cell ratio (T4:T8) in cerebrospinal fluid is higher in patients with multiple sclerosis than in patients with other neurological diseases.

10. We will have a wound care specialist take a look at her stage II decubitus ulcers and see what can be done to help with that.

Chapter 18—Orthopedics/Neurology

1. She is noted to have crepitus with flexion and extension of the knee.

2. Examination of the lower extremities revealed 2+/4 to 3+/4 reflexes in both knees.

3. He was able to forward flex the neck to 60 degrees and extend to 40 degrees, with rotation of 80/80 degrees and tilting of 30/30 degrees.

4. ADMITTING DIAGNOSIS: Tensor fasciae latae syndrome, left thigh.

5. PROCEDURE: Austin bunionectomy with 0.045 K-wire fixation.

6. DIAGNOSIS: Salter II fracture.

7. There was evidence of degenerative disease at C5, C6, and C7.

8. EMS brought the patient to the ER fully intubated with a GCS of 5.

9. Immediately after identifying the Scarpa fascia, a very loose connective-type tissue was identified.

10. The subcu portion of the wound was then irrigated and skin margins approximated using 4-0 Vicryl stitch.

Chapter 19—Obstetrics/Gynecology/Pediatrics

1. Bimanual pelvic examination revealed normal adnexa.

2.
POSTOPERATIVE DIAGNOSES
1. Status post previous cesarean section.
2. Macrosomia.

3. Delivery produced a viable male infant with Apgars of 8 and 9 at one and five minutes.

4. Cervix was 5 cm, completely effaced, and at 0 station.

5. Two of 50, or 4%, of the cells examined were monosomy X (45,X).

6. The patient is gravida 2, 1-0-1-1.

7.
DIAGNOSES
1. Pregnancy of 38 weeks' gestation.
2. Estimated date of confinement 3/18/2006.

8. This is a 24-year-old Hispanic female, gravida 1, para 0, who presented at an estimated gestational age of 40 weeks by dates and confinement.

9. This baby was born following a 27-week gestation to a 32-year-old, gravida 2, para 1-1-0-1 mother.

10. Abdominal ultrasound revealed a 12-week viable fetus with an anterior placenta and a 2 cm cyst on the right adnexa, which is probably a corpus luteum cyst.

Chapter 20—Ophthalmology

1. LOCS II under slit-lamp examination revealed grades NCII, NIII, CIII, and PII.

2. There was a II-2-3 isopter area on Goldmann field assessment.

3. After repeat neodymium:YAG capsulotomy treatment, the diplopia disappeared.

or

After repeat Nd:YAG capsulotomy treatment, the diplopia disappeared.

4. There were abrasions 2-3 DD just inferior to the optic disc.

5. She presented with a chief complaint of photophobia in both eyes.

6. Ocular adnexa are within normal limits on examination.

7. Cup-disc ratio was measured at 0.25.

Chapter 21—Organisms and Pathogens

1. He was diagnosed with Human immunodeficiency virus (HIV) in 1999.

2. There are approximately 40,000 cases of salmonellosis reported in the US every year.

3. Cultures were diagnostic for Streptococcus pneumoniae, which later proved to be resistant to both cephalosporins and macrolides.

4. Escherichia coli is often contracted from a contaminated water source, though the patient could not identify a likely contact.

5. The patient reports she became a vegetarian while living in Wales during the "mad cow" scare.

6. Due to her advanced encephalopathy, she is unfortunately now a Child-Pugh class B.

7. The vaginal swab culture was positive for group B beta-hemolytic streptococci.

8. Blood cultures came back positive for gram-negative bacilli.

Chapter 22—Psychiatry

1. The patient is about a 50 on SOFAS, unable to keep a job due to personality conflicts with her coworkers and apparently has few, if any, friends.

2. Neither Mattis Dementia Rating Scale nor Mini-Mental State Examination revealed any significant concern for early dementia.

3. On my examination, she exhibited some contradictory communication, bouncing around randomly from one topic to the next.

4.

DIAGNOSIS

Axis I	Attention deficit hyperactivity disorder (ADHD).
Axis II	None.
Axis III	Asthma.
Axis IV	Father deployed in Iraq.
Axis V	GAF 75.

5. Her sister reports the patient is mostly "manic" with occasional depressive episodes.

Chapter 23—Pulmonary/Respiratory

1. EMS initially gave him 6L of O2 [or O_2] by mask, then titrated this back to 3L when respirations returned to baseline.

2. PFTs revealed an FEV1-to-FVC ratio at 30% of predicted.

or

PFTs revealed FEV_1-to-FVC ratio at 30% of predicted.

3. She is being maintained on 3L O2 [or O_2] by Ventimask.

or

She is being maintained on 3L O2 [or O_2] by Venturi mask.

4. Temperature 98.7, BP 134/82, and respirations 18 per minute.

5. Room air gas showed a pH of 7.27, pCO2 of 38, and pO2 of 85 with 95% saturation.

or

Room air gas showed a pH of 7.27, pCO_2 of 38, and pO_2 of 85 with 95% saturation.

6. We have ordered a V/Q scan to assess perfusion.
7. FEF25-75% [or $FEF_{25-75\%}$] was 0.13 L/sec.
8. Due to anaphylactic response, the patient had a class III airway, and it took several attempts at intubation to secure an open airway.
9. He was a 17 on the Epworth assessment and was referred for sleep study.
10. Blood gas analysis done on room air showed a pO2 of 63, pH 7.42, pCO2 44, and actual bicarbonate of 28.2.

or

Blood gas analysis done on room air showed a pO_2 of 63, pH 7.42, pCO_2 44, and actual bicarbonate of 28.2.

Chapter 24—Other Specialty Standards

1. There was artifact on the film, so we will need to x-ray the knee again.
2. She has a history of non-insulin-dependent diabetes mellitus.
3. We ordered plain films of the abdomen and pelvis.
4. On MRI, the apparent diffusion coefficient of each necrotic or solid contrast-enhancing lesion was measured with two different b values (20 and 1200 s/mm^2).
5. We have been correlating the T2 relaxation times on MRI of specific brain regions in schizophrenia.
6. DIAGNOSIS: Type 2 diabetes mellitus.

Appendix B
AHDI Product Catalog

Other Great Products from AHDI!

The Book of Style for Medical Transcription, 3rd edition
$50.00 members
$70.00 nonmembers

The 3rd edition of The Book of Style for Medical Transcription from the Association for Healthcare Documentation Integrity (AHDI) is now available in print and in a web-based electronic version. This widely acclaimed industry standards manual has long been the trusted resource for data capture and documentation standards in healthcare. The 3rd edition delivers a streamlined and strategically reorganized flow of critical data, enhanced explanation of standards and practical application, robust examples taken from clinical medicine settings, and so much more.

The CMT Review Guide
$52.76 members
$65.95 nonmembers

The CMT Review Guide is an excellent resource manual to prepare for the CMT credentialing exam. Every core content area of the CMT exam is topically addressed in this text. In addition to transcription standards and style, English language, medicolegal and privacy issues, and the healthcare record, *The CMT Review Guide* takes an organized approach to medical language by providing learning objectives and over 50 review questions (20 in print, 30 on CD-ROM) for each major body system covered on the exam. With this systematic approach, the test candidate will gain the confidence and competency needed for successful exam preparation and performance. Purchase directly through Stedman's (www.stedmans.com) or through the AHDI online store (www.ahdionline.org).

The RMT Review Guide

$52.76 members
$65.95 nonmembers

The RMT credential is a Level 1 designation and is designed for practitioners based in physician offices, those working only with certain specialties, and also for the graduating medical transcription student. Highlights include:

- 3 major units of study (Medical Language, Systems/Specialties, & English Language)
- Sample reports in each chapter
- Review questions to access your preparation level
- Bonus CD including 360 additional review questions!

Purchase directly through Stedman's (www.stedmans.com) or through the AHDI online store (www.ahdionline.org).

Mega MT Challenge I & II

$35.00 members, $45.00 nonmembers (Each individual CD)
$60.00 members, $80.00 nonmembers (Combo Deal)

These electronic CDs contain over 1200 questions (combined) related to the practice of medical transcription. You'll find questions pertaining to medical terminology, English fundamentals, pharmacology, and an array of medical specialties. A broad variety of question formats (including multiple-choice, true/false, circle one, fill in the blank, etc.) are designed to fully test the wealth of knowledge essential to the practice of transcription. Whether used for self-study, exam preparation, evaluation, staff training, potential employee testing, or classroom instruction, these products are designed to help meet those needs. Order online or by phone.

CMT Prep Quizzes, Volume I

$25.00 members
$35.00 nonmembers

CD contains a whopping 240 exam-style questions, answers, and descriptions as found in archived publications. This interactive CD allows you to take the quiz on screen, view the answers and descriptions, and (for CMTs seeking CE credit for recredentialing) print a score sheet at the end of each quiz. In addition to some great level II prep questions, this product will also give CMT candidates practice with on-screen test taking. *Approved for 12 Clinical Medicine CECs.* Order online or by phone.

CMT Prep Quizzes, Volume 2

$25.00 members
$35.00 nonmembers

CD contains a whopping 240 exam-style questions, answers, and descriptions as found in archived publications. This interactive CD allows you to take the quiz on screen, view the answers and descriptions, and (for CMTs seeking CE credit for recredentialing) print a score sheet at the end of each quiz. In addition to some great level II prep questions, this product will also give CMT candidates practice with on-screen test taking. *Approved for 12 Clinical Medicine CECs.* Order online or by phone.

Willie Getwell

$25.00 members
$35.00 nonmembers

This CD provides proofreading and editing exercises designed to enhance your skill in the area of editing and error recognition. You will find 40 transcribed and speech-recognized drafts to orient you to the unique editing and proofing process associated with both domains. Product is perfect for getting your editing up to speed before testing. *Approved for 15 MT Tools CECs.* Order online or by phone.

Multiple-Choice Assessment Workbook

$25.00 members
$35.00 nonmembers

Multiple-Choice Self-Assessment can help MTs evaluate their knowledge in six major content areas. Previously used in preparing MTs for Part I of the CMT exam, this module consists of 60-multiple choice questions, arranged randomly in one section and by content area in a second section. Answer keys and content codes provided. Three-hole punched booklet (8-1/2 x 11) for easy storing. Order online or by phone.

CMT Prep Assessment Online Course

$100.00 members
$125.00 nonmembers

Offered every month of the year, this four-week course is designed to assist individuals preparing for the CMT exam. Course offers assessment in over 20 body systems. Each body system covered will list websites, medical texts, and references from *The Book of Style for Medical Transcription, 3e,* where applicable. Register online or by phone.

RMT Prep Assessment Online Course

$75.00 members
$100.00 nonmembers

Offered every month of the year, this four-week course is designed to assist individuals preparing for the RMT exam and offers assessment in the areas covered in the RMT exam blueprint. Register online or by phone.

Medicolegal CEC Bundle

$15.00 members
$20.00 nonmembers

AHDI ***CEC Bundles*** are a power-pack of creditworthy information and accompanying quizzes to assist credentialed MTs in earning those important CECs, especially when your credentialing cycle is drawing to a close and you need those last-minute, hard-to-earn credits. Each bundle consists of a zipped file containing the following documents in .pdf format: **2 articles, 2 quizzes, and 1 crossword puzzle.** Each bundle *is approved for 3 CECs* in the designated category. This medicolegal bundle contains 2 credit-worthy articles, 2 quizzes, and 1 crossword puzzle on the following medicolegal issues: ***HIPAA and the New ARRA Regulations*** and ***The Health Story Project***.

Medicolegal Flashcards

$25.00 members
$35.00 nonmembers

AHDI ***Flash Cards*** are designed to provide the student, new graduate, and/or seasoned MT with quick, high-impact study tools for skill-building and exam preparation. Take this handy, convenient pack of easy-to-use flash cards with you when you travel, have a long wait in a doctor's office or kids' soccer practice, or just need to make the most of that 10 minutes between appointments. Each set of flashcards covers a content area on the AHDI exam blueprint and is designed to put that core knowledge right at your fingertips. This set of medicolegal flash cards will test your knowledge and understanding of a broad range of medicolegal concepts and terms associated with the healthcare delivery and the documentation sector including such topics as: ***HIPAA, document types, document formats, the legal record, malpractice, DNRs***, and many more.

TO ORDER ANY PRODUCT ABOVE, VISIT WWW.AHDIONLINE.ORG. You can also call AHDI at 1-800-982-2182 to place an order by phone.